Daddy

I Want To CoMe HomE.

PleaSe geT me.

LoVe,

JASON

1. ALABAMA
Late Bloomer—Peg Sutherland
2. ALASKA
Casey's Flyboy—Vivian Leiber
3. ARIZONA
Second Wife—Stephanie James
4. ARKANSAS
Bittersweet Sacrifice—Bay Matthews
5. CALIFORNIA
Hunter's Way—Justine Davis
6. COLORADO
Rafferty's Choice—Dallas Schulze
7. CONNECTICUT
Special Delivery—Judith Arnold
8. DELAWARE
Taking Love in Stride—Donna Clayton
9. FLORIDA
Marriage by the Book—Joan Johnston
10. GEORGIA
Baby, It's You—Celeste Hamilton
11. HAWAII
Daddy's Girl—Barbara Bretton
12. IDAHO
One of the Family—Kristine Rolofson
13. ILLINOIS
Above Suspicion—Andrea Edwards
14. INDIANA
Intrusive Man—Lass Small
15. IOWA
Count Your Blessings—Kathy Clark
16. KANSAS
Patchwork Family—Carla Cassidy
17. KENTUCKY
Heart's Journey—Cathy Gillen Thacker
18. LOUISIANA
Crazy Like a Fox—Anne Stuart
19. MAINE
Fantasies and Memories—Muriel Jensen
20. MARYLAND
Minor Miracles—Rebecca Flanders
21. MASSACHUSETTS
Only the Nanny Knows for Sure—Phyllis Halldorson
22. MICHIGAN
The Proper Miss Porter—Ruth Langan
23. MINNESOTA
Emily's House—Nikki Benjamin
24. MISSISSIPPI
Beloved Stranger—Peggy Webb
25. MISSOURI
Head Over Heels—Leigh Roberts
26. MONTANA
Renegade Son—Lisa Jackson
27. NEBRASKA
Abracadabra—Peg Sutherland
28. NEVADA
Chances—Janice Kaiser
29. NEW HAMPSHIRE
Racing with the Moon—Muriel Jensen
30. NEW JERSEY
Romeo in the Rain—Kasey Michaels
31. NEW MEXICO
Desperate Measures—Paula Detmer Riggs
32. NEW YORK
Honorable Intentions—Judith McWilliams
33. NORTH CAROLINA
Twice in a Lifetime—BJ James
34. NORTH DAKOTA
Letters of Love—Judy Kaye
35. OHIO
One to One—Marisa Carroll
36. OKLAHOMA
Last Chance Cafe—Curtiss Ann Matlock
37. OREGON
Home Fires—Candace Schuler
38. PENNSYLVANIA
Thorne's Wife—Joan Hohl
39. RHODE ISLAND
Somebody's Hero—Kristine Rolofson
40. SOUTH CAROLINA
The Sea at Dawn—Laurie Paige
41. SOUTH DAKOTA
Night Light—Jennifer Greene
42. TENNESSEE
Somebody's Baby—Marilyn Pappano
43. TEXAS
The Heart's Yearning—Ginna Gray
44. UTAH
Wild Streak—Pat Tracy
45. VERMONT
MacKenzie's Baby—Anne McAllister
46. VIRGINIA
First Things Last—Dixie Browning
47. WASHINGTON
Belonging—Sandra James
48. WEST VIRGINIA
The Baby Track—Barbara Boswell
49. WISCONSIN
Fly Away—Pamela Browning
50. WYOMING
The Last Good Man Alive—Myrna Temte

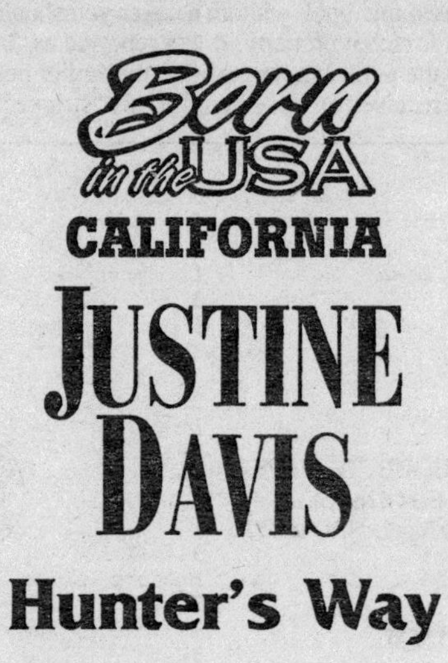

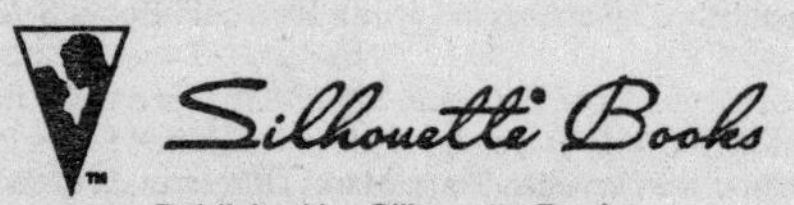

Published by Silhouette Books
America's Publisher of Contemporary Romance

SILHOUETTE BOOKS
300 East 42nd St.,
New York, N.Y. 10017

SBN 0-373-47155-6

HUNTER'S WAY

This edition published by arrangement with Harlequin Books S.A.

Printed in U.S.A.

Dear Reader,

It hardly seems possible to me that it's been over five years since my first book, *Hunter's Way,* was released. Even after writing over thirty books, it all seems new to me. I hope that's a feeling I never lose. My thanks to all the readers who have made it possible for me to experience the sheer joy of doing something I love for a living: being a storyteller.

I'm delighted that *Hunter's Way* is being reprinted in the BORN IN THE USA series, especially since it is set in my home state of California. I've lived here all my life, and can safely say there is no place else like it on the planet. You can go snow skiing in the morning and bake on the beach in the afternoon. Mountains, desert, sea, forest—California has it all.

There is an air of health and happiness in much of the Golden State, and this is one of the things that makes California such a great setting for stories. Especially stories with a darker edge, stories that contrast with the sun and light. So with *Hunter's Way,* I began with Hunter Garrett, a California cop with her own way of doing things, and one of the darkest of all scenarios, a missing child....

I hope you enjoy my "firstborn." I've come a long way since then, thanks to wonderful, loyal readers like you. I'll keep telling stories as long as you want to read them.

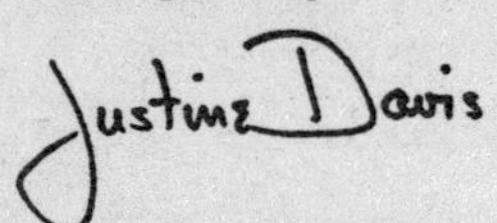

To Mary Fay,
who taught us we really did have wings.
To Judy,
who taught me how to use mine.
And to Tom,
who is the wind beneath them.

Chapter 1

"I think we should call the sheriff's office."

Josh Kincaid watched silently as the heavily jowled man behind the desk immediately tensed at the tentative words that came from his subordinate, Sam Singer.

"We can handle this," Victor Curtis grated out.

"I didn't say we couldn't." Josh's gaze switched back to the younger man, who went on with the air of one who knew he was digging a deep hole for himself but had no choice. "I just meant Garrett is the best."

The minute he saw Curtis's florid face redden even further, Josh decided he'd had enough of this. He turned sharply, his steel blue gaze riveted on Sam Singer.

"The best?"

The words were clipped and uttered in the deep, powerful voice of a man used to being listened to. The other two fell silent instantly. It was a familiar reaction that Josh took for granted without stopping to analyze; it just happened. He'd never truly realized he was a man whose very presence garnered attention without his even having to speak. It wasn't just his physical stature, although his broad-shouldered, lean-hipped six foot two was imposing enough. It was his aura, a combination of confidence, power and a will so unwavering it was almost tangible, that made him such a dominant figure.

"Who," he asked impatiently, "is Garrett?"

"Sheriff's Investigator," Sam said when it became clear that his boss wasn't going to answer. "Specializes in these cases. Has an instinct about them, or something."

"Hmph!" Victor Curtis snorted. "Instinct, my butt!"

Josh caught the barest of twitches that pulled at Sam's mouth, and guessed that a rather uncomplimentary thought about Victor Curtis and the portion of his anatomy just mentioned had crossed the wiry young man's mind. But Sam only said, "Hell, we're just a little department and just getting started. This is too much for us, too high profile. We need the expert, or this whole thing could blow up in our faces. Hunter Garrett has the best rep in the state, Captain. You can't deny that."

"I don't care what—"

"Do it."

Josh's quietly spoken words left the furious captain no room for argument. They were not a request but an order, issued with force and what was called on the street command presence. Respect gleamed in Sam Singer's eyes as his boss reached angrily for the phone.

"Bet you're hell on wheels in that boardroom of yours," Sam murmured, too low for Josh to hear. But the blue eyes zeroed in on him anyway, and he smiled a little awkwardly as he added, "You'd make quite a cop, Mr. Kincaid."

The gaze flickered for a moment, but he didn't speak. Nor did he flinch even slightly when, moments later, the sound of the telephone receiver being hung up sharply echoed through the room.

"She'll be here in an hour," Curtis snapped at Sam. "This is your baby now, Singer. I want regular reports on your progress. From you, not from that...not from Garrett."

"Yes, sir," Sam replied dutifully, but it was said to Curtis's stiff back as he left the room. "Hope you haven't lost your touch, Hunter," he muttered, "or I'm in a lot of trouble."

Sam looked up to meet that steady blue gaze. He shifted in his chair, feeling pinned by those cool eyes, and when he spoke it was in the tone of a man driven to justify his actions in the face of his boss's reaction.

"He...he's got a problem about this." The eyes never wavered, and Sam shifted uncomfortably again before explaining in a rush. "The captain's old school. He should retire and get it over with.

The job as he knows it doesn't exist any more. Law enforcement has joined the twentieth century—he hasn't. Hardly proper loyalty to the department and one's superior officer, I know, but..." He stopped, then gave an awkward little shrug. "Hunter saved his tail once, bailed him out on a case that he'd blown from square one. He didn't like being proven wrong, especially by—"

"You've worked with this Garrett?" The interruption was so smooth Sam barely realized he hadn't finished his sentence. He nodded.

"Before Aliso Beach began its own police department, we contracted with the sheriff's office. A lot of our guys were with the S.O. but had been working this area for so long they decided to come over. I did. But the S.O. didn't want to give Hunter up. They like having somebody with a statewide reputation around."

Sam shook his head in wonder. "It's amazing. I wish I knew the secret, but I think it's something you're either born with or not." The man before him didn't look in the slightest need of comforting, but nevertheless Sam tried to reassure him. "If anyone can find your son, Mr. Kincaid, Hunter can."

"You'd better be right."

There wasn't a trace of threat in the evenly spoken words, but Sam suddenly felt like a man who'd been admiring a caged tiger, only to find that the cage wasn't locked. He glanced at the door, wishing that it would open and Hunter Garrett would step in to take this situation out of his lap.

When the door did open a little less than an hour later, there were three disparate reactions; from Sam, a barely audible sigh of relief; from Josh Kincaid, a brief flicker of surprise; and from the figure in the doorway, a slight widening of clear green eyes as they went from Sam to the tall, long-legged figure in the corner chair.

"Hi, Hunter." A grin began on Sam's face, but he quelled it, realizing any cheer under the current circumstances would be inappropriate.

"Sam."

The greeting, uttered in a pleasantly husky voice, was accompanied by a nod, then the green gaze zeroed in once more on the man now rising to his feet.

"You're Hunter Garrett?" Another nod.

In some small part of his brain that wasn't dealing with what had happened since yesterday, Josh Kincaid registered with rather detached amazement that facing him was the most striking woman he'd seen in a long time. Even in the fluorescent light of the office her neck-length hair gleamed, rich, red highlights shining amid the mahogany darkness. She had the fair, delicate skin that went with the light sprinkling of freckles over the pertly upturned nose. And her eyes...

He shifted his weight, suddenly aware that those incredible green eyes were sizing him up, and aware as well of an unaccustomed feeling of uneasiness, as if he were afraid she would find him lacking somehow. It had been a very long time since he had felt that way, and a gleam of respect came into his eyes as the thought that Sam might be right about her capabilities came into his mind.

As if she had found what she'd been looking for in her appraisal, the woman held out a slim hand to him. "Mr. Kincaid."

As he began to lift his hand, he acknowledged inwardly that he was pleased she wasn't wasting time on the usual trivial formalities. Then their fingers met, and despite years of cultivation, the usually unreadable mask he wore slipped as a little electric jolt raced up his arm. He stared at her for a second, stunned, but the woman released his hand and turned away, giving him no clue as to whether or not she had felt it, too.

"What do we have, Sam?"

"Not much," the other man said, handing her a thin file folder. "No call, no demands yet. But we thought, Mr. Kincaid being who he is..."

She nodded. Any missing person under the age of twelve was automatically placed in the "at risk" category, but when lack of evidence pointed to the contrary, a missing child was presumed to be just that—missing or lost, unless something turned up to change that. In this case the prominence and wealth of the child's father provided a motive strong enough on its own to move the case into the suspicious category.

She bent her head over the report, and Josh found himself fascinated by the slender column of her neck, bared by her hair, which fell forward in a shining mass. He was suddenly aware of the long, lithe lines of her body beneath the emerald green jumpsuit and the way they were softened into lush femininity by full curves. His body tightened in response with a speed that startled him.

Damn, he swore silently. What the hell was this? He stared at her, trying to understand. She wasn't classically beautiful; the sassy nose with its tiny freckles and the slight defiant set of her delicate chin saved her from porcelain perfection. Yet those very things, along with the vivid coloring of her eyes and hair, made her utterly fascinating and, above all, cracklingly alive.

You, he told himself scornfully, are imagining things. It's been too damn long since you've been with a woman. Then reality flooded back, and he cursed himself for his wandering thoughts. That icy mask slipped back into place.

Hunter Garrett stared at the report in her hand, not really seeing it. Before she'd left her office, she'd taken the time to ask a few questions and make a few calls about Josh Kincaid. She'd been told, in tones ranging from grudging to outright admiration, that he was a hard-nosed but honest businessman, a man who had won the respect of CEOs of companies twice the size of Kincaid Industries. And that he had gained nationwide attention for his work on a new weapons-and-explosives detector for airports, and he was the proverbial self-made millionaire at thirty-eight.

What they hadn't told her, she thought rather grimly, was that he was also over six feet of wonderfully distributed muscles, a devastatingly attractive male, with thick, dark hair and eyelashes to match. Who right now looked about as approachable as the moon.

She'd seen the color of those eyes before, she mused, in the blue spots of an iceberg. Yet when they had shaken hands, the shock that had run through her had awakened long-dormant nerve endings that were still tingling. This, she said to herself, was not going to be easy. Forcing herself to concentrate, she was finally able to read the report.

When she shut the folder at last, she glanced at Sam. He nodded and left the room without a word, closing the door carefully behind him. Leaning against the front of the desk, she turned to face the man whose gaze had never left her. When she spoke, it was with brusque precision.

"I have my own way of working, Mr. Kincaid. Sometimes it may seem odd to you, sometimes unproductive. All I can tell you is that it works. I—"

"Is that a guarantee?" His voice matched his eyes, cold and harsh.

She took a moment before answering. "As I'm sure you know, there are no guarantees in life. And fewer in police work."

"What's your success ratio?" He could have been in a business meeting, she thought, and again paused before answering.

"Eighty percent overall."

She hid her satisfaction at the momentary flicker in those eyes. She didn't feel it quite the time to point out that that percentage included those grim occasions when her success had not come in time.

"I will have to ask you some questions. You may not like some of them—"

"How is asking me going to help—?"

"Mr. Kincaid." She shot upright, and despite the six-inch difference in their heights, something in her voice, some steel core not quite hidden by the soothing, husky quality, made him take notice. "I said there are no guarantees, but I will make you a promise. If you persist in making this a power struggle, my investigation will terminate immediately. This is not your boardroom, nor is it an attempt at a corporate takeover. It is your son's life. If you are unable to deal with my methods, I suggest you save us both a lot of time and trouble by saying so now."

For the first time in longer than he could remember, Josh Kincaid was speechless. The only thing his stunned brain could think of in that moment was that if this little firebrand walked into his office looking for a job, he'd hire her in an instant. No one had stood up to him like that in years.

"I'm sure no one could rise to your level in business without knowing when to defer to the experts in a particular field," she said, her tone slightly softer. "Don't abandon a practice that has worked so well."

"You being the expert?"

"I am very good at what I do, Mr. Kincaid," she said simply.

There was a moment of silence, followed by a slow nod from Josh Kincaid. "Good. I have little use for people who don't know their own worth. What did you want to ask?"

His abrupt capitulation didn't catch her off guard; she had seen it in his eyes in the instant before he'd spoken. She returned to her position leaning against the desk.

"When did you last see your son?"

"It's all there in the—" He broke off. She knew it was in the report; she'd read it. "Eleven-fifteen last night," he said, his voice carefully even.

"He was up at that hour?"

His eyes locked on hers, but the green depths were shuttered, unreadable, and her voice held no accusation. "No. He's only nine years old, as you know." He paused, trying to rein in the sarcasm that was creeping to the surface. "I looked in on him when I got home from the office."

"Are you often that late?"

"What has that got to do—?" Again he broke off. He was finding this harder than he had expected; he was not used to answering to anyone for his time. "Yes."

"Do you have any idea where your son is?"

He stared at her. "What in the hell—? Why would I be here if—?"

"The last case I had, the father knew all along that the child hadn't been kidnapped. He held it back to teach his wife a lesson."

Josh laughed harshly. "No, I don't know where he is. And it would have taken more than that to get through to my wife."

"Would have?"

"She's dead."

There was no grief, no pain in the deep voice, and Hunter didn't waste time on platitudes that were obviously not needed or wanted.

"Then Jason lives with you full-time?"

Josh noticed the omission and was surprised at the relief he felt at not having to fend off the traditional, meaningless condolences. He was more grateful for her perception than he had ever been for those useless words.

"Yes," he answered, "except for a month in the summer that he spends in Hawaii. His grandparents live there."

"Your parents?"

"His grandparents," he repeated. "His mother's parents are dead."

"You've checked with them, I presume?" How odd, she thought, referring to your parents only as your child's grandparents. It told her a great deal about the relationship between Josh Kincaid and his parents.

"Yes. They've heard nothing. I didn't tell them."

"Of course. No sense in worrying them yet."

He looked at her coldly. "You are laboring under a delusion, Investigator Garrett. They are incapable of worry, unless it's about themselves. When I said Jason spent a month there, I was referring to the place, not them."

"I see." The iceberg eyes, she thought, were apparently an inherited trait. And she'd been right about the relationship—or lack of one—between this man and his parents. "What about any friends, any place he might have gone?"

"No. He wouldn't. Not without getting permission."

She held back a grimace. How does a nine-year-old ask an iceberg for permission? she wondered. "Mark Twain once said that it's easier to beg forgiveness than ask permission," she said casually.

He looked at her rather oddly for a moment, then shook his head. "Not Jason."

She accepted that for the moment; she had no other choice. "When did your wife die, Mr. Kincaid?"

"Seven years ago." He said flatly. "My son doesn't remember her."

And you wish you didn't, she guessed. This was not getting any easier.

"What does your son do when he's not in school?" For the first time, Hunter saw a trace of emotion in those piercing eyes. Guilt, perhaps?

"What all nine-year-olds do, I suppose. Plays. Watches television." She said nothing. "My work takes up a great deal of my time. I don't—" He broke off sharply, his eyes narrowing as he looked at her. When he spoke again, his words were like chips off that iceberg she kept thinking about.

"What I do with my time is not at issue here. My son is missing, and I would like to know what you are going to do about it."

Hunter met his frigid stare unwaveringly. "Take my investigation elsewhere," she said shortly. "I'm not into pulling teeth." Then she walked out of the room.

Josh stared at the door she had quietly closed behind her. If she had slammed it, indicating some level of anger, he might have found the situation easier to deal with. But her calm exit left him with the distinct impression that he was worth neither getting angry at nor wasting her time on. It was a feeling he'd left behind long ago, and he didn't like this abrupt, jarring reminder. Rage surged through him and he headed for the door. Nobody talked to him like that, he'd—

He froze in the very act of turning the knob. He'd what? Spin his wheels in some useless dispute while Jason was out there somewhere, maybe in trouble, or hurt? Argue with the person who was trying to help find him? The person who, despite her unexpected appearance, according to all evidence had the expertise to do it?

This is not your boardroom. Her words echoed in his mind. She was right. He had been treating this as if it were one of his meetings. His jaw tightened. No matter how much it galled him, he needed her help. He had spent a lifetime not needing anybody's help, but he needed hers. For Jason.

In the outer office, Hunter hung up the phone and concentrated on making a brief note in the margin of the report she'd just read again, this time committing most of it to memory.

Sam had done his usual thorough job, she thought. The report was complete, a local broadcast had been made and the information had been entered into the National Crime Information Center's massive computer banks, all well within the legal time limits. The Department of Justice's required release form for dental records and X rays was there, signed by Josh Kincaid in a bold, flairing hand, and amended by a comment in Sam's writing that there were no available X rays but that the dental records had already been requested. She flipped back to the front of the file, and to Jason's photograph, which she had saved for last. She picked up the pencil to make another note requesting an enlargement of the picture.

She didn't need to see the expensively cut, elegant silk suit or the gleaming gold of the watch that banded a tan, muscular wrist to tell her who was standing in front of the desk. She'd sensed his presence the moment he'd left Curtis's office.

"Power struggle?"

Her pencil stopped midstroke. Only the years of practice she'd gained in her work kept her face expressionless. Slowly, assessingly, she raised her eyes. The suit was exquisite, but only because it did little to hide the lean, hard body beneath it. Whatever Josh Kincaid did outside his office, it kept him in great shape.

Her eyes slid over his broad chest and up the strong, corded muscles of his neck. The strength of his jaw was softened by the line of his mouth, and the flint of his eyes was warmed by thick dark lashes, unexpectedly beautiful amid the set, forbidding lines of his face.

That contrast made her abandon the pretense of not knowing what he'd meant by those softly spoken words.

"Touché," she said, barely restraining the tug at the corner of her mouth. Surprisingly she saw an answering glimmer in his eyes, and she found herself wondering absurdly what he would look like when he smiled. If he ever did, she amended as the gleam faded.

"I...old habits are hard to break. I'm used to giving the orders."

I'll bet you are, Hunter thought. But she realized this was as close as she was going to get to an apology, and wisely elected not to pursue it. She merely nodded in acceptance of his words. It had clearly been difficult for him to go even that far.

"I've called your housekeeper. She's expecting me." She slid the report on Jason Kincaid back into its folder and stood up, giving his father a questioning look. After a moment he nodded.

"You can follow me to the house." He turned on his heel and strode off, leaving her to follow with a sigh. She restrained herself from voicing a caustic thank-you for his royal permission. That would no doubt shatter the tentative truce between them.

The house was exactly what she had expected. Huge, on a sprawling piece of acreage whose size screamed money in this wealthy section of town. Inside and out it looked as if it had been ordered out of a magazine and set down here intact, leaving some trendy interior designer with a bulging bank account.

It sat in the spring sunshine like an ad for the good life in southern California. Not a toy in sight, and not a leaf on the perfectly manicured lawn. A mere leaf wouldn't dare, Hunter thought dryly, rolling her eyes at all this immaculateness. Not much of a home for a child. Fingerprints on these pristine walls would probably be punishable by grounding for life.

The housekeeper was a pleasant surprise. Here, at least, was a source of warmth and comfort. Mrs. Elliott was a round, grandmotherly type, who nevertheless gave off an air of brisk efficiency. Right now, worry had replaced what Hunter guessed would normally be a perpetually cheerful expression.

"My, things have changed these days, haven't they?" She peered at Hunter a little doubtfully. "Aren't you a little young, dear, for this kind of work?"

"It ages you quickly," Hunter said with a smile. Something in her face must have convinced the older woman, for she nodded suddenly.

"Well. Now, you said on the phone you wanted to talk to me about little Jason. Oh, I do hope he's all right! I feel so guilty, I should have—"

"Shh," Hunter hushed her softly, taking the woman's hands. "It's not your fault. No one can watch a child twenty-four hours a day. Now, tell me about Jason, what his day is like."

Josh watched the exchange with an interest over and above his concern for his son. Gone was the scrappy fighter, the quietly confident investigator; this was a woman talking to a woman, urging with gentle persuasion that soothed even as it drew out every answer she wanted. Did she have children of her own? The sudden thought gave him an odd sense of disquiet, which he shoved aside to be analyzed later.

"Except for the afternoons he goes to the ball field, he's always home right on time."

"Ball field?" Josh came back to the present abruptly.

"Why, yes," Mrs. Elliott said, looking up at her employer. "You know, he was so thrilled that the bigger boys picked him to be their...oh, you know, Mr. Josh, the one who picks up everything and..." She floundered helplessly.

"Bat boy?" Hunter suggested, and the woman nodded eagerly.

"Yes, that's it! He's so proud."

The woman rambled on for a moment, but Hunter's eyes never left Josh Kincaid. That he had not known about this aspect of his son's life was obvious, although someone less experienced in reading faces might have missed it. He maintained a carefully even expression; only the merest flare in the clear blue eyes gave him away to her. She wondered what other revelations were going to occur before this was over.

After obtaining a few specific details about the last day the boy had been seen, Hunter got to her feet. "I'd like to see his room."

That she asked it of Mrs. Elliott, who had already clearly demonstrated that she knew much more of Jason's daily life than the child's own father, was not lost on Josh. And Mrs. Elliott's description of her actions when Jason hadn't returned home from school indicated that calling him had been a last resort. The knowledge stung more than he would have thought possible. Josh felt that anger simmering in him again. Things were slipping out of his control, and he didn't like it.

"His room? Certainly, Ms. Garrett," he said, making an exaggerated bow as he gestured widely toward the stairway. "Right away, Ms. Garrett."

He heard Mrs. Elliott's gasp of surprise at his rude tone, but Hunter just looked at him with one raised eyebrow. Once more he felt as if he were under a microscope, as if that penetrating green gaze saw through to his soul. He waited, expecting some scathing retort and not altogether sure he didn't deserve it.

"It's Mrs.," she said quietly, and started up the stairs.

Josh felt as if he'd been kicked in the stomach. He stared after her. He'd thought she might pointedly correct him with her professional title; that she had chosen instead to drop that personal bomb left him groping for words. Something, he thought in irritation, that is becoming a regular occurrence with her.

The logical, analytical part of his mind wanted to figure out why that announcement had such a tremendous effect on him, but he let his anger override it, all the while denying that he was intentionally ignoring the question. He headed up the stairs, feeding that anger with every step, until he was convinced that the sight of that trim, tight bottom a few steps above was having no effect on him whatsoever.

Jason Kincaid's room was as spotless as the rest of this hospital that passed for a house, Hunter thought as she glanced around. True, there seemed to be every toy imaginable, including a computer that would put to shame the one at her station, but every single item was in a select place, looking neat and tidy. Too tidy for a nine-year-old.

For the first time, Hunter felt some qualms about this case. She reached down to the crisply made bed—with hospital corners, no doubt—and picked up the only thing that seemed real to her—a worn, much-hugged, stuffed pony.

"Tell me, Mr. Kincaid," she said in a voice that suddenly sounded tired as she straightened to look at him, "does your son ever get dirty? Play in the mud? Bring home a frog in his pocket?"

Josh stared at her as she clutched the slightly threadbare toy as if it were as dear to her as it was to his son. A frog in his pocket. The words seemed to rip away the years, and he was back in his mother's living room, her elegantly kept living room that was strictly for company, being much too good for her own family. Not much older than Jason, Josh had stood there fighting tears as his mother's tirade rained down on him mercilessly, berating him for daring to bring his dirty self and that "slimy creature" into *her* house.

His jaw went rigid and he fought the memory, fought to hide the effect her chance words had on him. He cursed his own weakness. He had thought those images had been too deeply buried to ever surface again.

"That," he ground out when he could trust himself to speak again, "is none of your business."

"Everything about your son is my business." She spoke with emphasis. "And I'd like this room a lot better with a pair of dirty socks on the floor."

That she had hit a nerve was clear to her, and Hunter revised her original iceberg opinion. There was heat left in this man, but a heat kept so tamped down that it took a veritable calamity, such as the disappearance of his own son, to stir it up.

"And it's going to be my business," she went on flatly, "until he's back where he belongs." She glanced around the clinically tidy room. As much as any child could belong in this antiseptic place, she thought.

"You just do your job," he said coolly. "That does not include editorial comments on how I raise my son."

Hunter had heard it so many times it ran off her back like water off feathers. Everybody in the world thought they knew what a cop's job was—until it came time to do it.

"Who's your son's best friend, Mr. Kincaid?" she asked, knowing with sad certainty that he wouldn't be able to answer.

Fury blazed in Josh, and he had to fight for control. He didn't miss her implication that he was not the one raising the boy. Fear for Jason was a coarse rasp shredding his already frayed temper, and the searing, guilty knowledge that she was right snapped the last fragile strands.

"You just find him! And stay the hell out of my way!"

Each word was bitten off sharply, hot with barely contained rage, and Hunter wondered that she had ever thought him cold. She hadn't meant for any of those words to slip out, but she had seen it so often—the wealthy parents who thought that things were all a child needed to be happy.

Nice work, Garrett, she chastised herself as the angry man stormed out of the room. Very unprofessional. He had every right to get angry. And boy, did he get angry! With a sigh she turned back to the room and began with little hope to search for any clue to the boy's whereabouts.

What was it about that woman? Josh stood in front of the big picture-window that looked down the long, curving driveway of the house, not seeing any of it. How had she managed, in the space of three short hours, to make him so furious that his usual dispassionate composure had disintegrated not once, but three times? True, he was worried about Jason, but he still couldn't quite believe that anything was truly wrong. He half expected to see him coming up the driveway any minute.

As it gradually grew darker, his sense of foreboding increased. His efforts to convince himself everything was fine became weaker, and he had to turn what inner strength he had left to staving off panic.

He was still standing there in the now-dim room when Mrs. Elliott appeared, speaking rapidly as she opened the front door for Hunter. "—not usually like that, he's such a gentleman, he—" She broke off suddenly as she caught a glimpse of his shadowed form. "Why, Mr. Josh," she exclaimed, startled, "I thought you'd gone back to the office!"

"That seems to be the general opinion of my parenting concern," he muttered. The fact that open, honest Mrs. Elliott assumed he placed his work so far above his son's welfare bit deeply into the wound already opened by Hunter Garrett's verbal slash.

"I beg your pardon, sir?"

"Forget it," he said shortly. "And I don't need anyone to apologize for my behavior for me."

The older woman flushed, and he could have bitten his tongue off. His gaze flashed to Hunter. She merely looked at him as if he were once more a specimen on a slide, then turned back to the other woman.

"Thank you, Mrs. Elliott. Try not to worry too much. I'll let you know if we come up with anything."

She walked out the door without a backward glance.

It took a moment for Josh to realize that the unaccustomed heat he was feeling in his face was a blush. When he looked back at Mrs. Elliott, he felt as if he'd kicked a puppy.

"I...excuse me, Mrs. Elliott. I—"

"You hush now. I know you're just upset."

"That's no excuse for taking it out on you. I...apologize."

My God, he thought at her look of surprise, am I really so bad that an apology from me is such a shock? Yet he knew it was true. The awkwardness with which the words had come told him how long it had been since he'd spoken them.

He turned his head at the sound of a motor starting, and watched Hunter Garrett's nondescript unmarked car pull away. He had an odd feeling that what had happened here was just the beginning of a snowball tumbling down a powder-covered hill.

Chapter 2

Hunter ran slender fingers through the thick mass of her hair, which was already tousled out of its usual sleekness by several earlier repetitions of the same action. Her eyes began to move toward the clock, but she forced herself not to look, knowing it would be only five minutes since the last time she'd checked, even though it seemed like five hours.

Four days, she thought grimly, staring down at the pile of papers on the desk in front of her. Four days and not a hint of what had happened to Jason Kincaid. No call, no ransom demands.

Once more she buried the gut-level, instinctive feeling that had been growing since the day she had taken her first look at that too-clean room, and turned back to the seemingly endless list of possibilities.

Money, plain and simple ransom, was the most obvious one, but this much of a delay before any demand was made was highly unusual. Revenge? A disgruntled ex-employee, perhaps? With what she had seen of Josh Kincaid so far, it was not out of the realm of possibility. The man had been a thorn in her side ever since she had taken the case. These few hours here at Sam's desk had been her longest respite from him.

She couldn't help but smile slightly at her own thought. She supposed he felt much the same way. The look on his face yesterday when, in response to a panicked phone call from his personnel manager, he had strode into that office to find her digging through all his records for the past five years, was that of a man finding a pesky mosquito he was certain he had shooed away.

But he had also looked unutterably weary. The blue eyes that had been so penetratingly clear the day they met were now red rimmed and bloodshot, his face drawn and pale beneath the tan. It had been clear to her that he had had a long and probably sleepless night. Regardless of any outer appearances, she'd known in that moment how deeply Josh Kincaid loved his son. She'd tried hard to remember that when she'd been tempted to slap a pair of handcuffs on him just to get him out of her way.

In his office, he had grudgingly given her a list of possible names to begin with in her check of fired employees, but had stared in stunned surprise when she had begun to question him about his company's current work.

"You want what?"

She had sighed wearily. She had had no more sleep than he had, and knew it was only the first of many such nights. "Your company," she said carefully, "is on the leading edge of research and development for airport security. This new system of yours, the 'Eureka II,' if it can indeed detect plastic explosives and nonmetallic handguns, could put a large kink in the activities of any number of terrorist organizations. We can't discount the possibility that there may be a connection."

He had stared at her, amazed. Although not top secret, that system was not general knowledge. The lady had clearly done her homework. And, he had had to admit reluctantly, she had a point, one that hadn't yet occurred to him. Abruptly he had told her to wait and left the room.

It gave her the chance she'd been waiting for, the chance to inspect the office that had so surprised her when she'd entered it.

It was large, lit by sunlight streaming in through a huge window, and obviously decorated by a professional hand. But the similarity between the office and the house ended there. Here, the perfection of decor was pleasantly marred by signs of life—a stack of folders on the desk amid the clutter of pencils and pieces of paper marked with the bold, dark flair, several blueprints spread out over a large table in one corner and expensive chairs pressed into service as holdalls.

But what had drawn her attention the most were two totally unexpected things: a beautiful sculpture of a rearing horse in heavy crystal that sent the sunlight skittering around the room in little rainbow arcs, and a framed photograph that sat on the corner of the desk.

The photo was of a child, about two, perched on the broad shoulders of a man, secure in the strong hands that held him, a look of joyous laughter on his innocent face as he tugged on a lock of the thick, dark hair beneath his hands.

Despite the difference in Jason Kincaid, she recognized the child immediately from the photograph that had been with the report. The natural changes that had taken place in a growing child were expected; the changes that had occurred in the man were shocking. Any resemblance between the exultant figure looking at the child above him with love and tenderness, and the man she'd met three days before, was physical only.

Her keen hearing had picked up his even stride as he neared the office, and she was back in her chair by the time he came through the door. Wordlessly he handed her a folder, inside which she discovered a copy of a business magazine's report on Eureka II, a financial newspaper clipping on its effects if successful, and a prospectus put out by Kincaid Industries.

"That's all that's been released on it, all that would be available to the public. If anybody has more, there's a leak. I don't think there is." She had nodded, showing no reaction to his clipped tones. If she hadn't seen that picture...

She heard a door slam somewhere and was jolted out of her reverie. She must be tired, she thought, to drift off like that. Determinedly she reached for her stack of notes and dragged herself back to the present. They had set up recorders on both Kincaid's office and house phones, and had checked and rechecked the security systems at both places. Everything was functioning properly and, as she had expected, was technologically the most advanced available.

After that she and Sam had begun the drudge work, the long round of interviews that made up the backbone of any investigation. They had talked to every member of Jason's class, every teacher at his school. This morning Sam had started going to every home between the school and the house, while Hunter had gathered her poise and tackled the baseball team Mrs. Elliott had mentioned.

She had endured with an unflappable grin the howls and wolf whistles the teenage boys rained down on her, along with the typical comments about being glad to get arrested if she was the cop. She'd almost wished she'd waited until their coach, who was gone for a couple of days, had returned. Perhaps he might have kept them under better control.

She tugged out the notes she had taken at the time, chuckling at the little sketch she had made of the most leering of the lot, the tall, skinny boy the others had called Dirk. He seemed to have been trying his best to shake her poise with rather lurid glances and off-color suggestions, but Hunter had handled worse in her years with the department, and it didn't faze her. She'd heard it all before and had let them get it out of the way before she had begun to question them.

She studied the notes, trying to figure out what it was that bothered her. Perhaps it was just a cynicism earned through years in a job that concentrated on the unpleasant side of human nature, but she found it hard to accept that a group of sixteen and seventeen-year-old boys had put up with a nine-year-old just because he was "hanging around all the time."

Perhaps when Rob Barrington, the oldest boy on the team—the "poor little rich kid" Dirk had called him, just as he had called Jason the "poor littler, richer kid"—returned, she could find out more. The consensus had been that he had more or less forced the rest of them to accept Jason's presence. Must be tough, she mused idly, having to spend your weekend in Aspen. Even with your parents, the bane of most seventeen-year-olds' existence.

"Here. I thought you might need this."

Hunter stared at the cup of coffee that had appeared on the cluttered desk, then raised her eyes to the man who had placed it there. He looked ghastly. The strain was really beginning to show.

"I suppose it would be superfluous to ask how you got in here?"

Josh Kincaid shrugged. "I ran into Sam Singer outside. He told me you were still here and let me in."

Thank you, Sam, she thought dryly. "Oh."

"He also said you haven't been home since you got here. That you've been sleeping here, and not much of that."

"It's the way I work. Sam knows that. And Captain Curtis decided now was a good time for a vacation, so I have his couch all to myself." Her mouth quirked slightly. "He doesn't like me much. An attitude I'm sure you can sympathize with."

Something like an answering glint of humor flickered in his eyes. Then he glanced at the clock on the far wall of the office, across the sea of desks that were empty at this late hour. "It's nearly eleven. Have you eaten?"

She masked her surprise. "No. I don't have much of an appetite when I'm on a case like this."

"You've got to eat."

"Afraid I'll collapse before I find your son?" She hadn't meant to sound so biting, not when he was obviously making an effort to be civil. For a change. "I'm sorry. That was uncalled-for."

He looked at her for a moment with an odd expression on his usually impassive face, then merely nodded. "Come on." The expression that came and went in her eyes warned him he was back on that thin ice again; his peremptory issuing of orders rather than requests had already sparked more than one tense moment. He tried to soften it by adding, somewhat ruefully, "Please. Since we can't seem to carry on a conversation, we'll be forced to eat."

She hesitated, then got to her feet. If he wanted to declare a truce, she was more than willing to accept. She needed all the help she could get in this investigation that seemed to be going nowhere.

She felt a little odd, sitting in his luxurious car as they drove just a few blocks, but she was even more taken aback at the place he picked. Chuck's Burgers did not look like the type of place that the Josh Kincaids of the world frequented. But at the delicious aroma that met her nose as they went in, her stomach growled unexpectedly and she hastily revised her opinion.

"I used to come here a lot," he said after they had ordered, looking around the small, crowded dining area with an expression she could only, however unlikely, describe as wistful. The words were quiet, low, as if he wasn't aware of saying them aloud. "I couldn't afford much else." He shook his head and let out a short, harsh chuckle. Hunter could almost see the current situation come flooding back to him. "I should have stayed that way," he said bitterly.

"Stop it!" Hunter snapped, and he looked at her sharply. "Could you have?" she asked, green eyes boring into startled blue ones.

This woman made him feel a little slow on the uptake all too often, he grumbled inwardly. "What?"

"Could you have stayed that way?"

"I..." He trailed off, seeing immediately the truth of what she was saying. The man, the boy really, he had been in those days could no more have resigned himself to that life than he could have flown. "No," he said quietly. "I had too much to prove."

"Then don't blame yourself for something you had no choice about. You'll go crazy if you start that. You'll drown in the 'if only's.'"

What the hell? Josh shook his head. Hunter Garrett looking at him so coolly, dissecting him under that microscope was one thing; this woman, vehemently rescuing him from a pit of self-condemnation, was something else altogether.

The food arrived, and Hunter found to her surprise that she was halfway through the sizable hamburger before she began to slow down and appreciate its taste.

"This is really good," she said in surprise.

A half smile tugged at one corner of Josh's mouth, and Hunter stopped in the act of reaching for another crisp fry. Lord, she thought, I was right. If he ever let loose with a full-on grin, he'd be lethal.

"Where'd you get the name Hunter?"

She realized with a little shock that he hadn't touched his own food, that he'd been steadily watching her. It made her oddly uneasy. "It's...a family name. My mother's maiden name, actually. Strange for a girl, I know—"

"I like it," he cut in, with that little smile again. Hunter hastily lowered her eyes.

"Thank you. Sam says it fits me," she added, her mouth twisting into a wry smile of her own. "I think he's got some romanticized vision of me as the 'great hunter' of missing persons or something."

Sam, Josh thought with sudden realization, has a plain old romantic vision of you, period. He wondered how many others were dangling after this little spitfire, waiting....

"Do you always put in these kind of hours?"

"The pot calling the kettle black?" She looked at him warily. "If you mean are you getting special treatment, I'm afraid not, Mr. Kincaid. Every case is special to me."

"Your husband must be...very understanding."

Hunter knew she hadn't mistaken the thinly veiled edge in his voice, although the reason for it escaped her. "That's where you're wrong. He didn't understand at all."

"Didn't?"

"He's dead."

He looked stunned, she thought, all out of proportion to the words she'd said about a man he'd never known.

"I...when?"

"That, to borrow a phrase, is none of your business." She couldn't help the sharpness in her voice. This was not a subject she discussed with anyone, let alone someone who had the knack Josh Kincaid had for aggravating her.

"Touché," he said softly, and to her amazement her anger drained away. He abandoned his questions then, and began on his own meal, seeming to be entirely wrapped up in his own thoughts.

Hunter sat back after she finished, turning over and over in her mind all the things that just didn't fit. No call, no note, nothing. Jason Kincaid had gone to school as usual, behaved exceptionally well, as usual—of course, he wouldn't dare not to—and left with the other children. He had just never come home. That gut-level feeling rose in her again, and she lifted her eyes to the man across the table from her.

"Mr. Kincaid," she began hesitantly, stopping when she saw that tiny hint of a smile again. It was a bittersweet contrast to the haggardness of his face and the dull worry in his eyes, and she couldn't quite put a name to the feeling it gave her.

"We've spent the better part of three days together," he said quietly. "Do you think you could call me Josh?"

This unexpected softening in him strengthened that odd, unnamed feeling, and made it even more difficult to go on.

"All right...Josh." She drew in a breath, and then took the plunge. "Have you considered the possibility that this may not be a kidnapping at all?"

"What do you mean?"

"I mean, what if Jason just...ran away?"

He stared at her. "What," he said carefully, "would possess you to suggest that?"

"Just a feeling. But it won't go away."

"A feeling?" His voice rose sharply. "You suggest my son is so miserable he would run away from home, and all you can say is you have 'a feeling'?"

"Based on fact. Your son has everything a child could want, but not what every child needs. A parent who's...there."

"Just what the hell do you know about it?" Josh snapped explosively.

And as easily as that, the tentative truce was shattered. Hunter sighed. "A lot. Based on years of experience."

"Years?" The sarcasm bit deep. "What are you, all of twenty-five? Experience," he snorted angrily.

"I'm thirty-one," she said, suddenly tired of his continual doubt. "And I've been doing this for six years." That seemed to slow him for a minute. He looked at her as if he were assessing her appearance in order to decide if he believed her. "I told you my successes were based on feelings like this one. When I've been wrong, it's been in cases where I haven't had them."

"Infallibility?"

She refused to rise to the bait. "Overall, no. Only when it's working." She got to her feet, tossing some money on the table for her meal. "Except," she added softly, not sure why, "the one time I wanted it most."

Josh stared at the door that had swung shut behind her. He felt a strange urge to go after her—she shouldn't be out there this late alone—then laughed ruefully at himself. She was a cop, and probably safer than he would be walking the few short blocks back to the station.

Then he caught himself. She had once again infuriated him, made him so angry he had turned on her, destroying the uncertain peace they had tacitly declared, and here he was worrying about her safety. It made no sense at all to him, and he shoved it aside to be considered later, becoming all too aware that the place in his mind where he held those things was becoming extremely crowded.

Could she be right? He remembered her comment that she'd like Jason's room a lot better with some dirty socks on the floor, and he cringed inwardly. Had he become that stern a taskmaster that his son was afraid of even that minor a transgression?

He picked up a cup of coffee that had already grown cold, then set it down without even tasting it. A memory of a day when he had joined Jason in the big pool in the backyard came to his mind. The same child who had been happily splashing back and forth across the pool became suddenly unable to swim a stroke, and had finally left in tears to hide in his room.

At the time, the obvious rejection had stung, and only now did a startlingly painful explanation surface. Had that tearful look been one of fear? Had his efforts to teach Jason to swim more smoothly been interpreted as dissatisfaction in his beginner's paddling? Had he become, in his son's eyes, impossible to please?

Hastily he stood up, suddenly wanting out of this place where so many unwanted memories had begun to stir. He tossed a bill down on the table, then halted when he spotted the folded money Hunter had left. Of all the women he'd ever taken out, few enough when spread out over the past seven years, he couldn't think of one who would have dreamed of paying her own way. He was Josh Kincaid, worth whatever it was these days, so he could certainly afford it.

Yet here, in this place where the entire bill was less than he had paid for one drink on occasion, Hunter Garrett had refused to let him take care of the check. Of course, it wasn't a date, he rationalized, but still the sight of that money made him feel decidedly odd. The feeling moved him to pick up that five-dollar bill and, for a reason he did not at all understand, tuck it into a corner of his wallet.

He walked out to his car, wondering what she had meant by "the one time I wanted it most."

Chapter 3

"You're sure there wasn't anything different about him that day?" Hunter tried not to press the already harried woman in front of her, but she was getting desperately tired of spinning her wheels.

"Not that I saw," the teacher answered. "He's always such a good boy, never any trouble."

"What about that day in general, Miss Talbot? Did anything at all happen out of the ordinary?" The young woman shook her head slowly. She was obviously distressed over the disappearance of one of her students; her slightly chubby face was drawn into lines of worry. "I know you've been through it before," Hunter said in gentle understanding, "but would you tell me once more all you can remember about that day?"

"It was just an ordinary day." She brushed a strand of sandy blond hair behind one ear and began to tick items off on her fingers. "We said the Pledge of Allegiance, I took roll, we read from the history text, then recess—"

"Nothing happened then?"

"No, nothing unusual. Then we did some math work—Jason is very good at that, you know—before lunch. No," the woman answered, anticipating the question, "nothing happened at lunch that I know of, either. Jason was fine. We did some artwork, and then the children worked on the stories they've been writing. Then I read to them. I do that last," she said by way of explanation. "It seems to keep them from getting too restless just before time to go home. We're doing *Charlotte's Web*."

Hunter smiled. "How is Wilbur these days?"

Miss Talbot smiled suddenly, and it lit up her plain face.

"I had a teacher like you," Hunter said, "who had me on tenterhooks day after day to find out if Charlotte could save him. I've always remembered the story. And her."

"That's what it's all about, isn't it?" the woman said with quiet enthusiasm, and Hunter felt a sudden kinship with the woman.

"So, Miss Talbot," she began after a moment, "is—"

"Call me Erica, please." Her brief sidetracking had clearly won the woman over completely.

"All right, Erica. That's it? After that they went home?"

"Yes. After the announcements."

"Announcements?"

"Yes, you know, the things that are coming up, some things they're supposed to tell their parents about." Her smile widened. "We leave it till the end in the hopes that some of them might actually remember part of it when they get home."

"Do you recall what that day's were?"

She thought for a moment. "Just that there was a film in the multipurpose room the next day, that parents' night was coming up and the start of the paper drive."

"Parents' night?" Hunter asked thoughtfully.

"Yes. The parents are invited to the school to meet the teachers, see the classrooms and the work in progress."

"Has Jason's father...ever attended these?"

"Mr. Kincaid? Oh, no, I don't think so. I understand he's quite busy. Jason say's he's a very important man. He's very proud of his father, you know. Says he's trying to make the world safe from bombs and things."

Hunter had to clamp down on her emotional response to the picture that was forming in her mind. She followed Erica to the classroom to retrieve the stories the teacher had mentioned. She wanted to read Jason's just in case there was something in it that might help. Every step of the way she couldn't help thinking of a lonely, nine-year-old boy who was so desperately proud of his father yet made excuses for his absence from his life.

It was an image the short, childishly worded yet meticulously written two-page story did nothing to dispel. She had told them, Erica said, to write a fantasy, about anything they wanted, the only restriction being they had to use human beings as the central characters. Hunter had scanned some of the other stories, amazed at what had poured out of those active little minds, but when Erica had handed her Jason's to read, she felt her heart twist inside her.

Jason Kincaid's idea of a fantasy was a house with a mother and a father and a little boy they both loved, even when he was bad. Period. No spaceships, no invasions, no magic, just a loving family.

"May I keep this?" she asked shakily. At Erica's nod, she tucked it into the folder that was growing uselessly thicker. She sat for a long time under the big oak tree in front of the school, waiting for Sam to finish his last recheck of the neighbors in the area before coming to pick her up.

Sam Singer ran a hand nervously through his sandy brown hair. He hadn't counted on Josh Kincaid being home when he stopped by to see Mrs. Elliott. They had nothing new to report, but Hunter had asked him to drop in and reassure the woman who was as close to a mother as Jason had that they were still working on the case full steam.

And he had walked almost into Josh Kincaid's six-foot-plus of muscle. A little tensely he had given the spiel he'd intended for the housekeeper.

"So what you're saying is that you're no closer to finding my son now than you were days ago," Josh said coldly.

"Well, these things take time—"

"Time? My son is God knows where, and you tell me these things take time?" Sam felt that same pinned sensation he'd felt that day in Curtis's office. "And where is this supposed expert of yours while this time is passing?"

Stung, Sam lifted his head. "You may be a big wheel, Mr. Kincaid, and I'm just an underpaid cop, but I'm going to tell you right now that you'd better lay off Hunter Garrett. She's the best at what she does, and she's your best shot at getting your son back unhurt. She doesn't need some high-and-mighty bigwig telling her how to do her job. She learned it the hard way."

Sam paused for a breath. Josh had been a little startled by the normally mild-mannered detective's explosion, but now he held up a hand as Sam seemed to be gathering steam to go on.

"Take it easy," he commanded, thinking that he'd been right in his guess about how Sam Singer felt about Hunter Garrett. Sam flashed him an angry look, but he said no more. "What do you mean, she learned it the hard way?"

Sam studied him for a moment before he said it. "By trying to find her own son."

Josh gaped at him, thinking he'd been flabbergasted more in the past few days than he had been in years. "Her son...was missing?"

Sam nodded. "Six years ago. He was two years old."

Six years. Josh recalled what she had said about having been at this for six years. "So that's how she got started," he said softly, more to himself than to Sam. Then what the other man had said suddenly registered. "He *was*...?"

"She found him. Too late."

Josh had half expected it, but it still hit him hard. *The one time I wanted it most.* Her soft words echoed in his head. "Oh, God," he murmured, unaware that he had uttered it aloud.

"Yeah," Sam said, that undertone of anger still in his voice.

"How...what happened?"

"Ask her if you want to know. I've already said more than I should." Hurriedly Sam made his exit.

Josh sat in silence a long time after he'd gone.

It was a blazingly glorious sunset, the kind southern California, particularly Orange County, was known for, but Josh didn't notice. He hadn't been aware of that kind of thing for days. Despair was no longer nibbling at the edges of his self-control; it was destroying it in large chunks. Along with his self-respect.

It had been unavoidably pounded home to him just how little time he had spent with his son. Beyond those moments when he looked in on him at night, or stared in puzzlement at the boy's bowed head on those rare occasions when they shared the big table in the dining room, he barely saw him. He knew nothing of his life, not even what he liked to do or wanted to be.

How had it happened? He stared at the photo on his desk, trying to understand how the two who had been so close in that picture had drifted so far apart. It happened because you let it happen, he told himself harshly. If Josh Kincaid was unforgiving of others, he was twice as hard on himself.

He was denied even the solace of the work that had always been his salvation in the past, for now he looked even at the office he loved with distaste. Had he been using it to escape the problem of his deteriorating relationship with his son? Or had it been the cause?

He reached out and abruptly slammed the framed picture facedown on the desk, unable to bear looking at it any longer. Grabbing his jacket, he headed through the deserted outer office to the elevator.

Hunter hung up Sam's phone with more energy than was necessary. Rob Barrington, she thought grimly, was a pompous, arrogant adult in the making. He had informed her with lofty imperiousness that he had got her message and if she wished to speak to him she would have to be there within the hour; he had more important things to do tonight than wait around. Yet she had no choice but to deal with him. He was the main connection between Jason Kincaid and the baseball team that had apparently been so important to him.

She was still steaming as she barreled out the door toward her car; running full-tilt into Josh Kincaid didn't help her mood any. In fact, it lacerated already taut nerves. She didn't like and didn't have time for the irritating way the slightest contact with him seemed to send those little jolts of awareness through her.

He was an extremely attractive man, but she was a professional, damn it, and supposedly immune to that kind of attraction. Which was hard to remember when his arms went around her to steady her against the solid wall of his body. So remember how he infuriates you instead, Garrett, she ordered herself silently.

She hadn't seen or heard from him since the night before, when she had walked out of the restaurant, and had been glad of it. She was in no mood for more of his sideways attacks, or for her own lack of control in responding to them.

"Not now, Mr. Kincaid," she said through gritted teeth as she pulled away from him. "It's already late, and I have an appointment with a seventeen-year-old who could give lessons in arrogance."

He didn't answer, and she looked at him more closely. Did even the mighty Josh Kincaid have a breaking point? He looked as if he'd passed it days ago. He hadn't shaved, although the rough stubble that darkened his jaw somehow didn't detract from his incredible looks. Neither did the tousled look of his thick, dark hair; in fact, the slightly shaggy effect only added to his already considerable appeal. Too bad he's got the temper of a tiger with a sore tooth, she thought wryly.

When he followed her to the unmarked car with the obvious intent of accompanying her, she turned around to face him.

"You've made it more than clear that you don't approve of me or my methods,'' she said carefully, ''so why subject yourself to something that so obviously pains you?''

''Because he's my son,'' he answered in matching tones.

He sat in silence as she drove, thinking about, as he had been for a long time, what Sam had told him. A picture of a younger and, if possible, feistier, Hunter Garrett had formed in his mind, only to be distorted by the very horror he was undergoing now.

He didn't look at her, determined to keep his cool from now on. Whether or not he agreed with her approach, as long as she continued to pursue all of the possibilities, he had no room to complain. And the absence of any kind of contact from anyone claiming responsibility for his disappearance was beginning to make him nervous in spite of the fact that he still couldn't believe Jason had really just run away.

The Barrington house, in the most exclusive section of the already exclusive little town, was grander than Josh's, although Hunter knew from her preliminary checking that Robert Barrington, Sr.'s, financial standing fell far short in comparison. A difference the junior Barrington was apparently aware of, if his hostile reaction to Josh's presence was any indication.

''Well, well, the big man himself!'' The sarcasm was not at all restrained. The boy's parents had gone on from Aspen to New York, and taken with them, it seemed, any need for their son to be civil. ''Did you just now notice the kid was gone?''

Josh tensed, blue eyes riveted on the cocky blond teenager. Barrington backed up a step for safety, but the fear that flickered in his eyes apparently wasn't enough to slow his tongue.

''Oh-ho! Feeling guilty, are we?'' he sneered. ''Gonna cost you a lot to buy your way out of this one, daddy. Buy him a car and driver maybe, or his own skateboard track? Anything to keep him out of the way. That's what guys like you are best at!''

''You little son of a—''

''Knock it off, both of you!''

Hunter whirled on Josh, whose mouth slapped shut in astonishment. ''If you can't keep it on a leash, go sit in the car. You get in my way, and I'll have you up on interfering charges so fast it will make your head spin!'' She caught Barrington's smirk and spun back around. ''That goes for you, too! You may still be a juvenile, but I can make your life miserable—count on it!''

A glimmer of respect came into the boy's eyes. Slowly he nodded, and when she spoke again, he answered her with relative politeness.

Josh was still fuming when they got back in the car: Hunter was admitting with no little amount of frustration that she didn't know much more than she had before. The boy had taken pity on Jason—she'd felt Josh tense at that, but he'd kept quiet—because he didn't seem to have anywhere else to go. He didn't know where he was now, hadn't seen him since a couple of days before he'd left for Aspen. "Probably got up the nerve to take off," he'd said, and only a warning look from her had kept Josh quiet that time.

Robert Barrington, Jr., she thought, was a very angry young man. And very likely the personification of the future Jason Kincaid, if things didn't change. And if he was ever found, she amended with an inward sigh.

They had just reached the street when a roar split the night from behind them, and a low-slung, racing type motorcycle jetted past them out of the Barrington driveway. Hunter caught a glimpse of blond hair as the bike wobbled and its rider nearly lost it in his effort to come as close as possible to hitting them without really colliding. An accident looking for a place to happen, she thought grimly.

"That arrogant little punk!"

The words burst from Josh as if they'd been in a pressure cooker.

Hunter masked her thoughts about a nine-year-old boy who was headed in the same direction and said only, "Yes, he is."

For some reason her quiet acquiescence irritated Josh even more. He couldn't help thinking she was putting him in the same category as the arrogant young Barrington. It put an edge in his voice when he finally spoke.

"So that's it. Looks like everybody agrees with you. Jason just ran away."

She kept her eyes on the road, schooling herself to ignore the tone of his voice. He had cause, she thought; this was eating him alive. "That is not 'it.' But it's becoming more likely with every day that passes without any contact or any ransom demanded, that it's not a kidnapping for money."

"Right," he said, the edge even sharper. "Even that...kid thinks he just took off."

"It doesn't matter what he thinks," Hunter said, maintaining an even tone with an effort. "We'll investigate everything."

"Since you've decided my son has simply taken off for greener pastures," he said wearily "why are you bothering?"

Hunter's hours of frustration suddenly boiled over. She'd had enough of arrogance, enough of this wealthy neighborhood that seemed full of people who thought they could buy their way through parenthood, and enough in particular of one stubborn parent who refused to see the truth about his own son's unhappiness. With a sharp jerk of the wheel, she yanked the car off the main road into a parking lot for a deserted park, pulling to a stop under a large, spreading tree and flicking on the interior lights.

Without a word she reached for the now-inch-thick file, extracting the paper she had got from Erica Talbot and handing it to him.

"That's why," she hissed through clenched teeth, and threw open the door and got out, stalking over to sit beneath the big tree, leaning back to look through the leaves at the silver half-moon that was bathing everything with its eerie glow.

Josh stared after her, then, when she faded into the darkness beneath the tree, shifted his gaze to the paper he held. He recognized the careful scrawl, and he felt his stomach tighten. He had to blink rapidly before he could read the title. "My Fantasy," it said, and he wondered what on earth was in it to set her off like that. Slowly he began to read.

When he came to her, Hunter didn't need any more than the moon's pale light to tell her that at last he understood. He wore the look of a man whose last props had been kicked from beneath him, whose last shelter had been torn away. That he was so late in coming to it made the arrival no less severe.

He dropped rather than sat down beside her, as if his legs had suddenly lost all strength. Crushed in a fist he seemed powerless to release was the little story that had torn him to shreds.

"I'm sorry, Josh," she said softly, unconsciously slipping into the familiarity he'd requested of her, "but you needed to know."

"All this time," he said brokenly in a voice she barely recognized as his, "all this time he felt like this and I...I never knew."

She saw him shudder and knew that all of Josh Kincaid's considerable defenses were in tatters. She saw him shudder again and saw the silvery reflection of the moonlight in the wetness that was suddenly tracking down his drawn cheeks. She wondered if he could even remember the last time he had cried, and her heart gave that tight little twist inside her again.

Driven by a need as old as time, a need to comfort a fellow being in pain, she slipped one slender arm around him. She half expected him to gruffly push her away. Instead, to her surprise, he seemed to crumple against her, and she felt the shudders intensify. Awkward, choking sounds rose from him, muffled by his effort to conceal them.

"It's all right," she whispered. "Let it go, Josh."

For a long time she just held him, knowing what havoc it had taken to bring this strong, proud man to this. The moon traveled a large part of its arc across the sky before the tremors that racked him eased, before she began to hear hesitant, harsh phrases that told of an inner torture too long endured.

"I love him, I really do. I just...it was so hard, after his mother...I hated her for so long. She never wanted him, except to use him against me. I knew what she was doing, but I still resented him for giving her that power over me.... I told myself he was part of me, he couldn't be at all like her, even if he looked so much like her it made me..."

It was rambling at first, but after a while the story began to come together for her, of a young man flush with his first success, infatuated with a glamorous, shallow woman who hated him for the fact that he had made her pregnant. He had done the right thing and proposed marriage. She had accepted, it seemed, for the sheer pleasure of making his life a living hell.

And then, when he had caught her once too often with one of her long line of lovers, and had told her she was headed for a penniless and childless divorce, she had taken her ultimate, warped revenge. After declaring to the world that he was a heartless, cold beast so that everyone would know he had driven her to it, she had swallowed a handful of tranquilizers.

"I...don't think she really meant to die...just to make me feel guilty, look guilty. But she messed up and took too many...." Hunter heard another harsh intake of breath. "Every time I looked at him, I saw her. I saw the hell of that marriage. I know it wasn't his fault she used him as a weapon. I never meant to blame him, to take it out on him...but I did. And then when she died...I couldn't seem to stop...."

He went suddenly rigid in her arms, twisting to look up at her with agonized eyes, his face still damp, his voice tortured. "Oh, God, Hunter, what if I...what if I never get the chance to make it up to him?"

"Shh. You will. You will," she soothed, wishing she felt as positive as she sounded. With an effort she controlled her own trembling, afraid of what it would do to him right now to sense her doubts. This Josh Kincaid, vulnerable, desperate, clawed at her emotions in a way she never would have guessed possible. She never would have guessed this Josh existed. Or that the sound of her name on his lips would make her feel so funny inside. It was a long time before either of them moved.

Chapter 4

The next day it was as if that Josh had been a dream, an illusion conjured up by moonlight and shadows.

She had asked him to come in and to go over the flyer she was preparing before it was released. While they had sent all the required information to the Department of Justice immediately, they had held off on a public release of information as long as the possibility of a kidnapping had been a strong one and there had been a chance of jeopardizing Jason's safety. If the boy had truly just run away, they had wasted precious time, but she knew they'd had no choice.

Her gut instinct told her the boy had done just that, but something was nagging at her, some feeling she couldn't pin down that there was more to this than she was seeing. But they couldn't wait any longer, she had explained to Josh.

Now, as he sat stiffly beside the desk in the office she had appropriated—with no small amount of enjoyment—from the absent Captain Curtis, she searched for any resemblance to the man she had held last night. She found none.

She could see the scars of that dreadful outpouring in the bleary redness of his eyes, heart wrenching in comparison to the clear, piercing blue that had been obliterated, and in the deepened lines of fatigue and pain that gouged the lean planes of his face into a silent witness to his inner agony, but his manner denied it. He was cool, formal and once more in rigid control. The iceberg was back.

Hunter smothered a sigh as she stared down at the picture of Jason that was to be put on the flyer. Josh sat silently; in fact, he hadn't spoken a word since he'd walked in, had merely taken the rough draft of the flyer she'd handed him and then sat down, avoiding even looking at her.

It was to be expected, she supposed. A man as strong and dominant as Josh Kincaid would not like the idea of anyone knowing he was capable of such weakness. And, she thought glumly, breaking down and admitting everything he'd told her last night would no doubt be classified as just that in his estimation. Was he one of those men, she wondered, who froze any tender feeling out of his heart because he thought it might make him less of a man? Or was he just a man who had put his feelings in a deep freeze to keep from being hurt, afraid to risk the pain again?

It didn't really matter, she told herself as she studied Jason's picture. She had never seen a picture of Cynthia Kincaid, but Hunter knew what she must have looked like from the honey brown of the boy's hair, the warm cinnamon of his eyes and the delicate shape of his face. It was hardly the boy's fault that he was the image of his dead mother, she thought. But it didn't matter, because either way the result was the same, at least as far as Jason was concerned. He had a father who couldn't, or wouldn't, show his love in the way the child, any child, so desperately needed.

So he had gone looking for it elsewhere. The words popped into her head seemingly of their own volition, and without really realizing why, her mind went back to Robert Barrington, Jr. Was that the explanation of their rather odd relationship? Had Jason found what he was lacking in the offhanded attention of the older boy? And had Rob found some missing sense of self-worth in the child's adulation?

She could, as she'd been able to ever since he'd sat down, feel Josh's eyes upon her, but she knew that if she glanced up she would only see them flick away rapidly. His determination to deny those poignant hours was complete, his icy shields solidly back in place. Unconsciously she bit her lip, wondering why he was staying. He—

The shrill ring of the phone interrupted her thoughts, and she answered it gratefully. It was the mother of one of Jason's classmates to say that the girl, who had been ill, was well enough to talk now, although she was sure there was nothing the child could tell her. Hunter was tempted to agree, but this was the only child she hadn't seen, and she didn't feel comfortable with even one stone unturned.

She acceded reluctantly to Josh's somewhat chilly request to accompany her, warning him that if he intimidated the girl, he'd spend the time sitting in the car.

"I won't say a thing," he said tightly. "Will that be satisfactory?"

"You don't have to say anything," she said dryly, and as his eyebrows drew together, added, "You obviously haven't looked at yourself from a nine-year-old's point of view."

In the car Josh sat in concentrated silence, his eyes fastened on the road ahead as he battled the urge to let them shift to the side to look at the woman driving. He was battling as well a flurry of emotions unlike any he'd felt in years, in fact, since he'd left home at sixteen. And not even then had he felt pulled in so many directions at once.

His anxiety over Jason was foremost, gnawing at him, eating away at him and replacing what it took with a crushing foreboding that threatened to rip him apart, and there was little room for anything else. Only the iron control he'd developed in the years since his wife's death enabled him to function at all.

Although he had forced himself to go to the office, he had accomplished little. He knew that eventually the business would suffer, yet he couldn't seem to care. He knew he should care, and that knowledge was one of the other things tugging at him relentlessly. He had built it up from nothing, had proven the world—and his parents—wrong, and now it was no more to him than an ineffective distraction.

Then there was that altogether too-effective distraction—the slender, vibrant woman beside him in the car. She alone was the source of more tangled feelings than he'd ever had to deal with in the carefully ordered life he'd set up for himself in the past seven years.

That she'd been the witness to, indeed had fostered with her gentle understanding, that emotional outpouring last night unsettled him tremendously. He couldn't remember the last time he'd broken down like that. That he had done it with her seemed both more disturbing and more soothing. The conflicting feelings added to his inner turmoil.

And aside from last night, there was the personal hell he'd been going through ever since he'd laid eyes on her for the first time. Josh Kincaid had little time for women in his life. When he felt the need, there were willing partners available to provide sexual satisfaction. If the fact that the payment was a fancy dinner or a trinket or two was only a variation on the more honest cash transaction occurred to him, he never let it bother him much. Both parties got what they wanted, he told himself, as in any other business transaction. If it was a little cold, he didn't mind; he preferred it that way. Warmth too easily became heat, and with heat came the inevitable burn.

Hunter Garrett had changed that. From the first moment he'd seen her, it had been impossible for him to maintain that cool impartiality; she seemed to stroke sparks off him by her mere presence. She was totally unlike the occasional women in his life. She refused to be intimidated by him, unlike most men and many women, and the thought of her playing up to him was patently absurd. He couldn't help admiring her, although he seesawed from wanting to strangle her to wanting to put his hands on her in an altogether different manner.

And that led to the final battleground within him, this one marked by the ugly banner of guilt. How could he even be thinking about a woman now? His only son, a small, defenseless child, was missing, was out there somewhere all alone, and here he was wrestling with adolescent urges he thought he'd left long behind. He hated himself for it, and hated Hunter Garrett for being able to do this to him so easily, without even trying. God help him if she ever did try....

A highly unlikely possibility, he thought as, despite his efforts, his eyes flickered to her. She was dressed casually today, in a T-shirt of some silky fabric of pale green that made her eyes stand out vividly and that clung lovingly to curves whose fullness was surprising compared to the slenderness emphasized by the snug, faded jeans she wore. He'd seen her chic in the emerald jumpsuit, elegant in a tailored suit and now effortlessly appealing in the all-American jeans and tennis shoes. He wondered which was closest to the reality.

She was biting her full, lower lip in that way he'd noticed before when she was deep in thought. The action did ridiculous things to his insides, which were already so confused that they'd forgotten their original purpose in life. He hadn't eaten for nearly two days. With an effort he wrenched his gaze back to the front, focusing intently on the dash of the car, as if it were the most fascinating thing in the world.

When they reached their destination, they found the little girl wrapped up in a bright, cheery red robe, her long, blond hair in a slightly lopsided ponytail— "I did it myself," was the solemn explanation. She tugged at Josh's already strained emotions. He didn't find it hard to keep his word to remain silent; he was afraid to open his mouth. He watched with intent interest as Hunter began to talk to the wary child.

"Are you really a police lady, like on TV?"

"Well, Jenny," Hunter said with a smile as she sat down on the sofa beside the girl, "I'm real, but I don't have nearly as much fun as they do."

Jenny appeared to consider this for a moment. Hunter drew up her legs and crossed them in front of her, elbows resting on her knees, looking for all the world like a teenager settling down for a long chat with her best friend. The child seemed to sense it, as well, and appeared to tune out her hovering mother, who was casting rather odd looks at the big man who sat in the chair by the window.

There was a flurry of paws and fur as a small bundle of tan energy erupted into the room and threw itself into the child's lap.

"Well, who's this?" Hunter asked with a grin as one brown eye peeped out from under the tangled mop of hair.

"This is Peanut Butter," the girl said cautiously, still not sure about accepting this stranger.

"Because that's what color he is, or because he likes it?" Hunter asked, to all appearances sincerely wanting to know the answer.

"Both," Jenny said, eyeing her with a little less suspicion.

"That would have been a good name for my dog," Hunter said, her grin widening. "He loved peanut butter, too. Once he got his head stuck in the jar trying to lick it all up."

Jenny giggled. "What was his name?"

"Stripe," Hunter answered seriously, "because he had spots."

This appealed immensely to the child's sense of the absurd, and in that moment her acceptance of Hunter was complete. Josh watched in amazement as Jenny opened up to her, chattering on about whatever Hunter asked. He winced when she touched on Jason, who was, the child said, her friend even though he was really quiet most of the time.

"He seems sad a lot, but he's always nice to me. One time he brought me a bone for Peanut. He liked to play with him. He said his dad wouldn't let him have a dog."

Josh froze at that. Jason had never even mentioned a dog. He'd never even known the boy had wanted one. As if sensing she had caused that sudden reaction, Jenny's wide brown eyes turned on him.

"He said it was okay, though, he didn't mind. He knew you were too busy for a dog. He was always talking about you." She turned back to Hunter. "He tried to keep a baby bird that once fell out of a nest, but it died. Jason cried, but I promised not to tell anyone that."

As Hunter hastily assured the little girl that it was all right, Josh clenched his jaw against the whirlwind building inside him. Once more it was being pounded home to him that he knew next to nothing about his own son, and that black slug of guilt expanded another notch. No wonder he ran away, he thought bitterly, his last reluctance to believe it smothered under the weight of that guilt.

Like a man shell-shocked, he followed Hunter out to the car when she had finished. He had no idea what had transpired during the rest of the interview. Mechanically he got into the car and closed the door, his eyes blank and unfocused as he continued his inward castigation.

"Josh?"

With a little jerk he looked up, only then realizing that she'd been talking to him. "I...I didn't..." He faltered, shaking his head. "What?"

"I asked if you knew about Jason riding with the boy on the motorcycle?"

"The...what?"

Hunter looked at him oddly. "What Jenny said, about Jason getting rides after school from some older boy on a motorcycle."

"She said that?" He stopped again, shaking his head numbly. "I guess I wasn't—" The sense of what she'd said suddenly penetrated. "Motorcycle?" His eyes narrowed. "Barrington?"

"Maybe," Hunter said noncommittally.

"You think he knows more than he told us?"

Hunter shrugged, not yet ready to put into words what was only a vague, uneasy feeling. "It might not even be him. But it's worth checking into, after we get the flyer circulating."

He nodded, settling back into silence until Hunter made a sudden right turn long before the street that led back to the small police station that had become her temporary headquarters.

"I need to make a stop," she explained at his look. She gestured to an open, grassy area up the street, which was, he saw as they drew closer, a baseball field surrounded by tall trees. "I've been trying to track that guy down for a couple of days."

Josh saw then that there was a young man there loading some

equipment into the back of a mud-encrusted four-wheel-drive pickup truck. "Who is he?"

"The coach of the team, with any luck. He matches the description, anyway."

Josh was two steps behind her as she trotted across the field, and only when he looked up to see the young man stop to watch her approach did he realize how raptly he had been watching the lithe movement of those long legs and the tantalizing tightness of her jean-clad derriere. The look of pure appreciation that spread across the young man's face irritated him, a feeling that intensified when she stopped and a pair of avid, dark brown eyes looked her up and down.

He whistled, a grin splitting his tanned face. "You have got to be the lady cop! The guys told me about you, but I didn't believe it until now." He held out his hands in mock surrender. "Take me away!"

"I forgot my handcuffs." Hunter grinned back at him.

"Too bad," he sighed in exaggerated disappointment. She laughed. He was so good-natured about his kidding she couldn't help it.

"You're Ed Sterling?" It was a formality; she was sure from the description she'd got. Very blond, very tall, very tan, and the girls loved him. She could see why.

"Even if I wasn't, I'd be a fool to say no," he said with a laugh, a teasing glint in his warm brown eyes telling her that he was purposely turning on the charm, that he knew that she knew it and he didn't care. It was impossible not to respond, and she laughed again.

Puppy-dog eyes, Josh was thinking acidly. Turn it on and off like a faucet. She ought to know better than to fall for that. "Can we get to the point?" he snapped.

"Who's the grump?" Ed never shifted his gaze from her face.

"Jason's father."

"Oh." The brown eyes flickered over Josh. "Sorry. Guess you've got a reason to be a grump." Somehow this did nothing to ease Josh's irritation. "He still hasn't turned up?"

"No. When did you last see him?"

"Last week, at practice. One of the guys called me last night after I got home, told me what happened. I've been gone all week." Hunter's eyes flickered to the truck at the curb. He saw her glance and nodded. "We went off-roading. There's my proof."

"I didn't need it," Hunter said mildly. Every instinct she had told her this young man had nothing to do with Jason's disappearance. She felt rather than saw Josh tense, but went on smoothly. "Isn't it kind of unusual for a group of boys that age to tolerate a nine-year-old hanging around?"

"I suppose, but Rob kind of forced it. He took the kid under his wing, sort of, said he knew just how he felt, parents never around and all. Anyway, since he's the big wheel on the team—"

"Big wheel?"

"Yeah. You know, the one with the fancy motorcycle, the big house for all the parties, that kind of stuff. The rest of the guys are pretty impressed with him." The brown eyes made the barest movement toward Josh. "They don't know yet that all that doesn't mean much."

Josh didn't miss the inference, and his growing irritation abruptly shifted to anger. But before he could say anything, Hunter was asking once more about Rob Barrington.

"I don't know. I always thought Rob had a reason for everything, you know, a...a..."

"Ulterior motive?"

"Yeah, that's it. He never did anything without figuring out how it was going to pay off for him first. That's why I was surprised when he took such a shine to the kid. But he seems to really like him. And so do the rest of the guys, now. He's a good kid."

This was said with another glance at Josh, but it did nothing to mollify him. Hunter asked a few more questions, and the young blond answered genially as he finished loading gear into his truck. At last she thanked him for his help.

"Any time, Officer. Or I mean deputy, I guess, don't I?" He grinned at her. "You ought to come by some time and watch the team. They're not half-bad."

"Thanks to their coach, I'm sure," Hunter said in a teasing tone that for some reason made Josh's anger rise another notch.

"Of course!" Ed's grin widened. "We've got a practice game at the high school next Monday," he said as he climbed into the driver's seat. "I'll save you a front-row seat."

"I might just be there," she returned cheerfully, waving goodbye as the muddy truck pulled away.

"Pardon me," Josh said through gritted teeth when she turned to head back to the car, "for getting in the way of your social life."

Hunter stopped dead, staring at him.

"Why didn't you just make a date with the guy? He was practically drooling."

"What's wrong with you?"

"I waste my afternoon while you and the beach bum play games instead of trying to find my son, and you want to know what's wrong?"

He knew he was out of line, but he couldn't seem to help it. He'd been walking a knife-edge for a long time, and he was finding it harder and harder to keep his balance.

"Your son," she said icily, "is my primary focus now, and has been since I agreed to help on this case. If I can get the information I need by acting like a human being instead of a...an iceberg, then I'm grateful for it."

"You call that little show you put on with that—"

"Ed Sterling is a very charming young man."

"Great," Josh snapped. "He's charming, so obviously he's innocent. He says he's been gone, so naturally you believe him."

"He said 'we.'"

"What?"

"He said '*We've* been off-roading.' As in company. As in not alone."

Josh shut up as it sank in.

"As in alibi," she said, somewhat unnecessarily. She knew he'd got it.

Stung that he had missed that obvious fact, his voice was harsh. "Fine. So he's innocent. The boy next door. Apple pie and—"

"What on earth did he do to you?"

"Nothing." Except be everything I never was. "I hope you two will be very happy together."

"At least he wouldn't be on my case every time I turn around," Hunter exclaimed in angry exasperation.

"No, he'd be too busy trying to make a move on you."

Her hold on her temper, rather frail since she'd met him, snapped. "I can think of worse things!"

He whirled on her then, grabbing her shoulders. "I'll bet you can," he grated out. "Like this."

His mouth came down on hers, crushing her lips against her teeth. She twisted in his grasp, a shocked sound rising from her throat. Instantly the pressure eased, his mouth became warm and urging, and she felt his tongue flicker softly over her lips. The sound that rose from her then had little to do with shock and everything to do with a rapidly awakening astonishment.

If Hunter had been startled at his action, she was stunned at her own reaction. After her startled cry, her every muscle had tensed, preparing for a defense she was more than capable of delivering. But something held her back; whether it was her knowledge of his inner turmoil or the sudden softening of his touch, she wasn't sure. She only knew that once she had decided not to fight him off, her ability to do it seemed to have vanished.

Instead, all her determination seemed to seep away into some rising, creeping warmth that was invading her limbs, sapping all their energy and diverting it to her suddenly pulsing, pounding blood. This is crazy, she thought vaguely, and tried to pull away.

Josh felt her move, and his hand went instinctively to the back of her head to stop her, his fingers tangling in the heavy silk of her hair in the way they'd been itching to do since he'd first seen the rich, burnished color of it. Insistently he deepened the kiss, probing with his tongue until at last, with a little sigh of breath, she parted her lips for him.

Josh nearly groaned aloud as his tongue slid into the warm, honeyed depths of her mouth. His body surged in response as she seemed to go soft in his arms and the heat of her seared him. God, she was so sweet, sweeter than he'd even imagined....

With a sudden convulsive movement, he pulled away sharply. He stared down at her, trying not to see how her green eyes had darkened, how her lips were still parted, looking swollen and full from his kiss.

"Damn you," he swore softly, and turned on his heel. He strode through the trees at the edge of the field and was gone.

Chapter 5

Hunter threw down the pencil wearily, and the little sound echoed through the room outside the office, empty on this Sunday evening. She hadn't been home, except to pick up some clothes, or to her own office except for a brief check to make sure everything there was under control. It seemed as if the car, this office and the couch on which she'd been sleeping, and the locker room downstairs where she took her showers were all that she'd seen in the past six days.

Which, she told herself severely, is probably better than what Jason Kincaid's been looking at. She picked up the pencil again and returned to the mass of notes, trying to compile them into some kind of chronological order. Then she rearranged them into what she called "people order," listing what pieces of information had come from what people, which more than once had yielded up a clue of some sort that she'd overlooked before.

Sooner or later, she knew, it was going to be out of her hands. With no evidence that this was a kidnapping or abduction, the case was eventually going to be classified as a straight runaway, at which point her department would no longer authorize her to spend any more time on it. "Give it back to the locals," her lieutenant would say, and she would have no choice but to do as he ordered. If she didn't find Jason before then...

She made herself concentrate on the papers in front of her, forcing her mind off Jason Kincaid's father. With great effort, she had pushed the memory of that searing, melting kiss into the category of emotional overreaction, both on her part and his, and had lectured herself severely on her lack of professional conduct. That she hadn't seen or heard a word from Josh helped, but—

The sound of a step brought her head up sharply. She knew before she looked up who it was. He came to a stop before the desk and stood there unmoving, his body rigid, his face hard and impassive.

"I owe you an apology," he said stiffly. "You have it. I also cursed you, and I apologize for that, as well. If anyone deserved that, it was me. I had no right—"

"All right," she interrupted. "Apology accepted." The clipped words were painful for her to just listen to. She could only imagine what it cost him to say them. Josh Kincaid had been through an emotional wringer these past few days. "We were both upset."

He nodded shortly, and Hunter sensed that there was something more, something else that was just as responsible for his mood. "What is it?"

He didn't seem surprised that she knew. He reached into the pocket of the battered leather jacket he wore and dropped an envelope on the desk in front of her. "Mrs. Elliott found it on the front door an hour ago." He sat down heavily in the chair beside the desk. "She didn't see or hear anything. She called me immediately. I called the neighbors on both sides. No one was home."

His voice was flat, inflectionless, as if he was reading statistics from a report. She sensed he'd had about as much as he could take. She looked at the note, saw that it had been opened and no doubt read by both the housekeeper and Josh. Still, she handled the paper carefully by the edges as she took it out.

It looked like a ransom note from every B-movie ever made, with letters, cut out from a magazine, glued crookedly into words. She stared at it for a long time, every instinct she'd developed over the years screaming out silently. She didn't even realize she was shaking her head until Josh asked her why, in a voice still harsh and labored.

"No," she murmured, still staring at the note.

"Another 'feeling'?" There was no accusation in his voice, just that strained tension, but she couldn't help remembering his first response to her feelings about this case. She answered him in brusque, businesslike tones, looking up to meet his gaze.

"Partly. Too many things don't fit."

The blue eyes narrowed. "Such as?"

"It's too late. In any genuine kidnap case I've ever worked, if there was a note it showed up almost immediately," she explained. She wondered why she was bothering; if someone didn't like the way she thought or worked, she simply closed them out of the investigation. "Anybody trying to pull off something like this knows it's too dangerous to wait."

"And?" he asked, his voice cool.

Hunter smothered a sigh. "The wording. It doesn't fit," she said again.

"I didn't realize there was a format for ransom notes."

"There isn't. But there are certain elements that are almost always present that are not here. It only says, 'If you want to know about your son.' There is no threatening of Jason's welfare, not even an implied warning. And," she continued, "the amount is wrong."

His eyebrows shot up, disappearing beneath the thick hair that persisted in falling over his forehead. "Wrong?"

"Too low."

"A quarter of a million dollars is too low?"

"When it's coming from a man whose net worth is forty—"

"I know my net worth, thank you." He cut her off abruptly.

"Then let me put it another way, Mr. Kincaid," she said, choosing her words with careful precision. "Just how much is your son worth to you, in financial terms?"

"What kind of a question is that? You can't put a price on—"

"Exactly."

He drew back in the chair, silenced by that one chilly word. Ignoring him, she turned her attention back to the note. After studying it for another minute, she reached for the phone.

"Sam? Hunter. I need— Yes, I know it's Sunday. I— Yes, I know what time it is. But I need this now. Kincaid got a note."

Josh winced at her casual use of his last name, as if he wasn't even there, but he told himself gruffly that he deserved it. She was speaking quickly, explaining to Sam what she wanted.

"—analysis on the paper. It's expensive stuff, with a ragged finish on three sides but not the top. It's not a standard size, so I think it might have been personalized stationery with the name and address taken off. That should narrow it down, especially if it was purchased locally. Also, the words on the note look like they're all from the same type of magazine. Same paper, maybe even the same issue. That may help."

She listened for a minute and made a couple of notes on a pad.

"Probably not. It's been handled a bit, but it's worth checking. We can get Kincaid's prints, and the housekeeper who found it, to eliminate them and see if anything's left." She paused for a moment, listening. "No, it doesn't feel right, but we've got to cover all the bases." Another pause. "I haven't asked, but I imagine he will pay it if it comes to that. But we're going to make sure it doesn't, aren't we?" she said pointedly, then listened to Sam's brief response. "Right. Thanks, Sam. I'll leave it in evidence-locker number twelve for you. Tell the boys at the lab they're back on my Christmas list."

Josh sat in silence, feeling decidedly humbled, a sensation he didn't care for and one he'd encountered far too many times since crossing paths—and swords—with Hunter Garrett. He had assumed, since she felt so strongly that the note was not genuine, that she wouldn't take it seriously, wouldn't pursue it. Once again he had underestimated her persistence, her thoroughness and her dedication.

She had barely put the phone down when it rang. He watched the expression on her face change and noted that her answers to the caller were carefully neutral, limited to "Yes," "No" and "I see." When she hung up after telling whoever it was she'd be there in thirty minutes, she intently began sliding the papers on the desk into a manila folder.

She stood, lifting one foot to the seat of the chair as she pulled open the center desk drawer. An odd sensation swept him, almost a chill, as he watched her pull out a short-barreled revolver in a black leather holster that she proceeded to strap around her slender ankle. With that one action, the reality of her work slammed home in his mind with stunning clarity.

He raised his eyes to her face, studying the fine line of her cheekbones, the thickly lashed, brilliant green eyes, wondering in disbelief if she'd ever had to use the small but deadly weapon. It was only after he'd been raptly looking at her for a few moments that he realized she was avoiding meeting his eyes.

"What is it?" he asked.

"Nothing. Sam's going to pick up the note and take it to the lab while I go check on something."

"You're a lousy liar. What is it?"

"Nothing," she repeated. "I'll let you know when anything turns up."

"That phone call—"

"Was routine. Excuse me."

She tried to walk past him, and he scrambled to his feet, grabbing her shoulders. The memory of that moment in the park leaped between them like a living thing, and he pulled his hands back as if they'd been burned.

"Hunter, please," he finally managed, his voice tight.

She sighed. "Josh—"

"Damn it, tell me!"

"All right! They've found a boy who fits Jason's general—I repeat, general—description. They want me to check it out."

The look of hope that had begun to appear on his face faded as her demeanor registered. He'd come to know when she was concealing something. "'They'?" he asked hoarsely.

"The coroner's office," she said gently.

He went white beneath the tan.

"Josh, don't. There's no reason to think it's him. It's just another lead that goes nowhere. I'll check it out and call you—"

"I'm going with you."

"No."

"Then I'll go alone."

"Josh, there's no need. I'll do it. If you're...needed, I'll call you."

He got to his feet without a word, moving as if he indeed was the old, old man who was suddenly looking out of his eyes. Deciding she'd rather have him where she could watch him, she gave in. She gathered the folder that was showing signs of wear, and led the way to the parking lot.

Since she was part of the sheriff's department that oversaw the coroner's office, she knew the place and its personnel much better than she cared to. Thankfully, on this Sunday night, the usually crowded area around the downtown Santa Ana complex was relatively quiet. She pulled in off Flower Street, parked in the lot designated for department vehicles and led Josh in through a back door. After threading their way through a maze of halls and a near-constant hail of greetings to Hunter, they reached a small lobby.

Going to the civilian receptionist, a new woman unknown to her, Hunter showed her ID and asked for the deputy who'd called her. The woman nodded and picked up the phone while Hunter urged

Josh to a worn sofa in the corner of the office and practically forced him to sit down.

It seemed much longer than the few minutes it took before a man stepped through the swinging double doors behind the desk and called to Hunter. Josh began to rise, but she placed a hand flat against his chest and pushed him back down on the worn cushion. He lifted a hand to remove hers, and she quickly knelt before him.

"Please, Josh," she said softly, urgently. The horrible visions of the too-frequent times she had been here before were etched in her mind as if with acid. Even if the body wasn't Jason, knowing that the next time it could be would only make the hell he'd been living worse by a hundredfold.

"I have to," he said stubbornly.

"No, you don't!" She grabbed both his hands. "Let me do it. I've got the dental charts for them to check. That will tell us if it...is or not."

"He's my son." He stared down at her hands over his.

"God, Josh, don't do this to yourself!" He refused to look up, and she lifted one hand to his chin to tilt it upward with a gentle finger. "Haven't you punished yourself enough? You've been through hell already—don't make it worse! And it will, believe me, no matter what's in there. Let me go. I'll tell you. I promise."

At last he met her eyes, and somewhere in the tortured blue depths was a touch of wonder. He shook his head slowly, as if in disbelief.

"Why?" he whispered. "I've been such...an idiot, why do you care?"

The urgency in her eyes softened, and an oddly quizzical look came over her face. "Darned if I know."

The silence drew out for a long moment, weary blue eyes locked on clear green ones that seemed to take some of that exhaustion into themselves. At last he let out a long breath, and taut muscles slackened as he dropped back against the creaking cushions. Hunter nodded in understanding and stood up, walking swiftly toward the doors before he could change his mind.

It seemed an eon later when she was leaning against the cool tile wall of the ladies' room, trying to control her stomach while she struggled to wipe the image of that innocent, dead face from her mind. She was torn by the horror of it, of that young life so easily snuffed out, and wondered how much longer she could keep this up. Every time, it brought it all back, all of the nightmarish memories, and every time, it was harder to shove them back into the cage in which they lived, barred and locked in the darkest recesses of her mind.

She pushed herself away from the wall with arms that were trembling. She had to go, had to get to Josh; he'd be going crazy by now. She forced her legs to move, to propel her through the doors, although she couldn't quite regain her usual steady stride. He saw her coming, saw the wobble and came to his feet with a look in his eyes that was somehow the worst thing she'd ever seen. It gave her the strength to hurry the last few steps.

"It's not, Josh. It's not Jason."

He gasped for air. "You...you're not just saying that? You're sure?"

"I'm sure. None of the dental work matches."

"But...you look so..."

"It's not a pleasant thing to do," she said harshly.

It hit him then, what she had done, what she had saved him from. At the cost of one more grim memory for herself, she had protected him from deepening his own despair, from taking one step closer to the edge he'd been hovering near for days now. A feeling he'd never known before welled up inside him, a feeling he couldn't name but was so strong it nearly surpassed the overwhelming relief her words had brought him.

"Let's get out of here," she said, and only when she turned to lead the way did he realize he'd been about to take her in his arms, to hold her, to try to thank her. Instead, he followed her silently outside.

He was so lost in the myriad of thoughts spinning in his mind that when the car came to a stop and she shut it off, he looked up in surprise. A surprise that grew when he realized they were in his own driveway, in front of the house that seemed ominously dark and cold. He turned to look at her.

"I think you've had about enough," she said quietly. "You need food and sleep. You won't do Jason any good if you collapse."

"Neither will you," he said slowly. He studied her for a moment, and Hunter thought that he looked almost nervous. Then she discarded the idea as absurd when he went on. "I make a decent omelet, if you don't mind breakfast for dinner."

She was startled but managed to hide it. "I used to work graveyard," she smiled. "I ate hamburgers for breakfast and waffles for dinner. Nothing seems strange to me."

He gave her the barest twitch of a smile. "Is that a yes?"

Knowing he would probably not eat a thing himself if she didn't agree, she nodded slowly and wondered how long the truce would last this time. Wordlessly they went inside, Josh leading the way and turning on a light only when they had reached the spacious kitchen.

Unlike the rest of the house, Mrs. Elliott's touch was evident here, her bright pot holders and cheerful flowers brightening an area that otherwise would have been as cold as the other rooms. Still in that odd silence, a companionable silence instead of their usual cease-fire, Josh began digging through the refrigerator. He stopped to look at her for a moment when, after studying the drawers and cabinets for a minute, she went unerringly to where the silverware and dishes were stored.

"Detective work?" he asked with a raised eyebrow.

"Actually," she said with a grin, "I just went to where my grandmother keeps everything."

He stared at her, a half-smothered chuckle escaping him, and then, unbelievably, he grinned back. A thousand-watt grin that, incredibly and unexpectedly, grooved his lean cheeks with a pair of flashing dimples. They took away the ten years he'd aged since she'd known him, and turned his severe good looks into a roguish attractiveness that was almost overwhelming.

Hunter nearly dropped the plates she'd found. My God, she breathed inwardly. I was right, but boy, did I underestimate! Hurriedly she turned away.

The omelet was considerably better than decent; it was delicious. He'd offered the formal dining room, but she'd shaken her head and said the breakfast nook, warm with Mrs. Elliott's flowered place mats and coordinated napkins, was fine with her.

"I don't blame you," he said as they ate. "The rest of this place is pretty grim."

She cocked an eyebrow at him. "You don't like it?"

He shrugged. "I never really noticed it. Until lately."

He paused for a bite, his eyes trained on her as she did the same.

"Relax," she teased. "It's great, as if you didn't know."

The grin again, slightly less wattage this time, but she wasn't sure the effect was any less.

"I..." He hesitated, glancing around the room and then back at her. "Cynthia—my wife—chose the place."

Hunter waited, not sure whether his words had been an explanation, an excuse or just a statement.

"I never did really like it. But she insisted, and I didn't fight her much in those days."

Hunter set down her fork, her eyes fastened on him. She didn't know what had brought on this softening in him, this crack in those formidable walls around his emotions, but she didn't want to risk interrupting it.

"We were...already on the outs then, but..." He lowered his eyes, and his voice dropped. "I'd promised her."

"Promised her? This house?" An odd promise to keep if the storm clouds were already gathering, she thought.

"It was part of the deal."

This was getting odder by the minute. "Deal?"

He took a long breath, then raised his eyes to hers. She saw the muscles in his throat ripple as he swallowed heavily. "She got what she wanted. I got my son."

Hunter looked at him blankly, not understanding. He saw it and chuckled harshly. "No, you wouldn't understand, not that kind of bargaining. Not you." That ghastly chuckle again. "This—" he gestured widely at the house "—is—what did you call it? What my son was worth to me, in financial terms. No," he hastened to add when he saw her look, "you were right—I had it coming. I usually do with you, it seems." His chuckle was rueful this time.

"Josh," she began, her confusion evident.

He held up a hand, halting her words. "This," he explained in a carefully even voice, "was the price for my son. She wanted an abortion. She said if I wanted the baby, it was going to cost me. Marriage and this house."

Hunter froze, staring. He had to be kidding. She searched his face. He wasn't kidding. She closed her eyes, pain welling up inside her, pain for the man before her and for the man he'd been. An image of the photo on the desk in his office flashed through her mind, and any sympathy she might have ever had for the manipulative Cynthia vanished forever in that moment. She couldn't believe anybody would bargain with the life of a child.

"Hunter?"

His voice held an odd, tentative note that she'd never heard before. She opened her eyes. He was watching her uncertainly.

"Whoever said you shouldn't speak ill of the dead had never met *her,*" she said through gritted teeth, practically spitting out the last word.

His uncertainty faded, replaced by a strange warmth whose source he couldn't identify. He only knew that it melted away an aching pain he'd carried around for years. The relief nearly staggered him, and he missed her low words.

"What?"

"Why do you stay here? In this house?"

"I'm not sure. At first it was for Jason. With everything that happened, uprooting him from the only home he'd ever had seemed too much. Then, when he started school and things got dragged out again, it was to prove something, I guess."

"Things?"

He sighed. "There were rumors going around at the time Cynthia died that I hadn't just...driven her to it."

"Oh, Josh," she said softly.

He gave her a sideways look. "The cops were okay about it. They said there wasn't anything to indicate she hadn't done it herself, and besides, I was in Denver at the time, had been for a week. I wasn't anywhere near—"

"Stop it," she interrupted sharply. "You don't have to give me an alibi. I know you would never do anything like that."

"Just like that? I say so, and you believe me?"

She met his gaze levelly. "You," she said, "may be arrogant, moody, stubborn and have the conversational tendencies of a clam, but a murderer? Not a chance, Mr. Kincaid."

His eyes widened at her words, but something in the softness of her voice took any sting out of them. "Are you feeling sorry for me or something?" he asked suspiciously.

"I can imagine people feeling a lot of things about you," she said with a small smile. "Pity is not one of them."

Before he could satisfy his curiosity about what other things she could imagine, she spoke again. "So why are you still here? Jason's old enough now. Why haven't you dumped this...mausoleum?"

"I'm not sure," he said, looking thoughtful. "Maybe I wanted it as a reminder."

"Of?"

"Of a lesson learned the hard way."

It took her a second to grasp his meaning. "Not everyone plays games with people's lives, Josh."

"If you'd told me that two weeks ago, I'd have laughed," he said ruefully. "Considering what's happened since, I should feel that way even more. But I can't, somehow."

Feeling suddenly uncomfortable with this lengthy peace between them, Hunter got up and began to collect the dishes.

"Leave them. Mrs. Elliott will be so glad I ate something, she'll be happy to clean up in the morning."

This was a Josh she'd never seen—calm, thoughtful, open and

much more human. It was a powerful combination, and for some reason it made Hunter edgy. When he was like this, she could too easily forget how quickly he could make her furious. She quit fussing with the plates, searching for something to say.

"She's been with you for a long time, hasn't she?"

"Since before Jason was born."

"Oh," she said, surprised. "Your wife...?"

"I hired her. I wanted Cynthia to have as little to do with him as possible, which suited her just fine."

"So Mrs. Elliott knows?"

"About our 'deal'? I don't think so. Cynthia was never mercenary in public. And I never told her." He paused for a moment, looking up at her as she stood next to the table, then lowered his eyes. His next words were so soft she almost didn't hear them. "I've never told anybody."

Hunter stared at the dark semicircles of his lowered lashes as they rested on his cheeks, her every muscle tensed. He'd never told anyone, yet he'd told her. Josh Kincaid had let down that iron control, had bared his soul to her. She wanted to reach for him, to touch him, and the thought frightened her. The cold Josh, the angry Josh, she could handle; this Josh she didn't know how to deal with.

"I...I should get going," she said hastily.

"Don't," he said softly, rising suddenly. "Not yet. You need a break. You've been pushing awfully hard." She stared at him. "I know," he said quietly, accurately reading her astonishment that he should suggest she take any time at all out of the search for Jason. "But like you said, you won't do him any good if you collapse. Just for a while. Please?"

She couldn't seem to find the power to resist him, and found herself beside him on a wide, cushioned bench in an outdoor gazebo beside the pool with no real recollection of having followed him outside.

"Jason likes to sleep out here in the summer," he said softly. "He keeps a sleeping bag under the seat."

"I can see why." She stared up through the lacework of the canopy to the scattering of bright stars overhead. She hadn't missed the undertone of pain in his voice, and after a moment she turned to face him. "You have to believe he's all right."

"I know."

"And that we'll find him."

"I know," he repeated softly. "You will."

She could only see the chiseled profile of his face in the dim light of the moon. She couldn't see his expression, but that new, gentle note was still in his voice, and it was still making her uneasy. Involuntarily her mind slipped back to that day in the park, that day when he had awakened feelings she'd thought long dead. She turned away, sitting quietly, trying to regain her composure. After a few minutes of silence, he spoke quietly.

"Hunter?"

She turned to face him, saw the gleam of moonlight in his eyes as he looked at her.

"What happened to your husband?"

For a moment he thought she wasn't going to answer, but then she said flatly, "He drank himself to death."

It was the last thing he'd expected, and he didn't know what to say. He wished he hadn't asked, hadn't given in to the driving need to know more about her. "I..." He faltered.

"It's all right. We'd split up years before. He couldn't handle my being a cop. He'd always hated it, but after—" She broke off abruptly.

"Your son?" he asked softly. She stared at him.

"Sam," she said finally. It wasn't a question, but he nodded. When she spoke again, it was in slow, measured phrases that were horrifying in their stark simplicity.

"Dan dropped Timmy off at preschool that morning. It was the last time anyone saw him alive. We didn't find him for five weeks. They said we were only two days too late. We never found the man who took him. The man who kept him in a dark, tiny closet for weeks before he finally—" Her voice broke.

"God, Hunter, I—"

"Dan took off a month later." She gathered herself and went on as if he hadn't spoken. "He came back once, to ask if I wanted a divorce. He was drunk. Said he'd been drunk for six months and planned on staying that way. A week later they found him in an alley. His blood alcohol level was point five-two. Over half. Impossible, they said. They couldn't figure out how he did it."

This time when she paused, he stayed quiet, as if knowing that any words from him would break the painful flow. He owed her that much, he thought.

"Two days afterward, I got a letter. From Dan. He'd mailed it just before he died. He said he...forgave me."

"Forgave you?" She had startled the words out of him.

"He'd always blamed me for Timmy. Said if I'd been home..." For the first time, her voice quivered, and it cut through Josh like a razor. Without even thinking, he moved, putting his arms around her and pulling her close. Still he didn't speak, sensing there was more to the horror. "Then he was furious because I...I couldn't find him. All the time I spent 'playing cop,' he said, and I couldn't even find my own son."

"God, Hunter, it wasn't your fault!" The words broke from him involuntarily.

"I know. But sometimes knowing isn't enough." He felt her move, felt her trying to gather the shreds of her control. He knew the feeling, the desperation, so very well, and his arms tightened around her. She stiffened for a moment, then seemed to go slack against him, and with a gentle hand he pressed her head to his shoulder.

"That's why you're so dedicated to your work, isn't it?"

"Maybe. I just don't want anybody to ever have to go through that if I can stop it." Her words were short and clipped now, sharp with remembered agony. "It's the worst pain in the world, and I can't just stand by and let it happen. I won't. And I won't let it happen to you."

This last sentence was said fiercely, protectively, and it gave him the oddest feeling of reassurance. Wherever Jason was, if it was humanly possible to find him, Hunter Garrett would do it.

There, in the starlit darkness, with her in his arms and the memory of that kiss in the park hot in his mind, he felt a wave of tenderness and desire so powerful it left him gasping, pulling in air in a long, gulping breath. That he wanted her, he'd known from the first minute he saw her. But this other feeling, this incredible melting warmth toward the woman he held, was now, foreign and so strong it unnerved him.

When she tilted her head to look up at him, her eyes filled with concern and determination, he couldn't stop himself from lowering his mouth to hers.

He knew in the first instant that that first kiss hadn't been a fluke. He'd been half-convinced, in fact had worked to convince himself that he had imagined the sweetness. But it was there, sending little tendrils of heat creeping through him. Then it changed abruptly as fire leaped between them, so sharp and swift that he was amazed he couldn't hear it crackle.

She made a tiny little sound, as if she'd felt that blaze in the same instant he had. Her hands slid up over his shoulders to lock behind his head, her fingers tangling in the thickness of his hair.

low rumble that was half groan, half sigh escaped him at the sensual tug of her fingers, and he tightened his arms around her.

He ran his tongue lightly over her lower lip, tasting, seeking, searching for the honey he'd barely sipped before. He felt the feathery brush of her breath as her lips parted for him, and a shudder went through him as his tongue darted into that beckoning warmth.

The warnings that went off in Hunter's mind were dim, distant and unable to penetrate the sudden haze of heat that had enveloped her. A heat that turned her to some soft, pliable thing to be molded by his touch. When his hands slipped down her back, she arched to him as if he'd demanded it. She heard him groan, but everything else was lost in her own gasp as her breasts, already heavy and swollen in a way she'd never known, rubbed against his chest. She felt her nipples tighten, and gasped again as the treacherous thought of what it would feel like if he moved his hands to them shot through her dazed mind.

The tiny bit of that mind that was still functioning tried to rationalize that it was only because it had been so long since she had kissed a man like this that she was melting so. But her soaring senses laughed at the feeble attempt. No man, not even Dan early on in their marriage, had made her feel like this with a mere kiss.

A mere kiss. Even as the words formed, she acknowledged the absurdity of them. There was no way that the maelstrom building inside her could be attributed to a "mere kiss." There was nothing mere about what Josh's mouth was doing to her. Shock at her own fierce reaction cleared away the haze.

Josh felt her stiffen in his arms and then try to draw back. He fought her for a moment before his own brain battled its way out of the pleasurable mist. He wrenched his mouth away, letting her turn her head, but he refused to let her withdraw completely. He pressed her head back to his shoulder and held it there until she relaxed once more.

"Josh," she began shakily.

"I know," he said, his voice hoarse. "Believe me, I know."

And he did. This was insane. He didn't want to feel this way, he thought desperately. He couldn't let himself feel this way. But it was so unlike anything he'd known before, he wasn't sure how to stop it. Or if he could stop it. Think about Jason, he ordered himself sharply, guiltily.

Yet he knew that he never really stopped thinking about Jason. Whatever he did, wherever he was, that gnawing fear was with him, feeding and growing with every passing hour. It was a hell he couldn't walk away from, as he'd been able to with Cynthia. It was a hell he couldn't control, as he did everything else in his life.

Almost everything. He still hadn't worked out how to master the conflicting mass of feelings that Hunter aroused in him, either. And holding her like this didn't help. He stared into the night sky for a long time, long after the smooth, soft rhythm of her breathing told him she was asleep.

He settled her more comfortably against him even as he tried to beat down his body's response to her nearness. He was still fighting his emotions when at last his weary mind surrendered and followed her into oblivion.

Hunter woke up with a start, tensing until realization flooded in. The first light of dawn was streaking the sky; she was still in the gazebo. That warm weight pressing against her was Josh.

She felt color flood her cheeks as she realized they were intimately entangled on the cushioned bench, her head pillowed on his shoulder, her leg thrown over his, his arm around her body just below her breasts. The flush deepened as she remembered. Josh Kincaid's angry kiss had been explosive, leaving her reeling in its wake. His tender kiss had been a creeping, glowing warmth that left her no doubts about how easily it could flare into an inferno. A dangerous, foolish inferno.

With slow care she freed herself, conscious of the solid muscle of his body as she moved. He stirred but didn't awaken, and she stood there for a moment, looking down at him as she shivered in the early-morning chill. He looked so weary, so worn, and so very, very young....

She went to the other seat and lifted it. Sure enough, the sleeping bag was there. She hesitated a moment, wondering if it would be a too-painful reminder of Jason, but as she shivered once more, she unzipped it and spread it gently over Josh. She stood there a moment longer, an odd expression on her face as she contemplated how well she had slept.

She was used to sleeping in bits and pieces while working a case; the hours of rest she'd got in his arms were a rarity. *In his arms.* The word sent a little shiver through her that had nothing to do with the cold. She stifled the urge to reach out and smooth back the stubborn lock of hair that fell across his forehead, and instead quietly went down the steps of the gazebo and toward the house.

Chapter 6

Hunter had pondered the idea of going to the baseball game Ed Sterling had mentioned for a long time. Finally the nagging feeling that she'd been carrying around for days, that somehow there was more than she was seeing in the connection between Jason Kincaid and the team, decided her.

She didn't get to the high school until the late innings, but Ed spotted her immediately and practically dragged her down to sit beside him on the bench.

"Too bad it's just a practice," she said, eyeing the scoreboard, which showed them to be ahead by five runs.

"Yeah," he said, flashing that easy, ever-ready grin. "Now if they'd just play like this when it counts!"

At that moment the hitter popped up for the third out, and Ed's team started in from the field for their at bat. Dirk Duncan saw her from the pitcher's mound and gave the expected wolf whistle before turning to spit what she presumed was tobacco juice rather blatantly in her direction. Not reacting, Hunter looked around.

She spotted Rob Barrington immediately. The tall first baseman stood out more for his dirty uniform than anything else.

"Rob really gets into it," Ed said, noting the direction of her gaze. "He's really intense. Almost angry, sometimes."

Just then the boy spotted her, and Hunter knew it wasn't her imagination that his trot faltered for a step or two. Or that he seemed to pale slightly beneath his tan. Was he just surprised to see her? Or was he nervous? That nagging feeling escalated abruptly.

By the time he reached them, Rob had recovered his poise and greeted them nonchalantly. If she hadn't seen it, she never would have guessed by his manner, as he teased Ed about hanging around with the heat, that her presence had disturbed him somehow.

"He seems fine now," she said casually after Ed had finished his instructions to his hitters and the boy was out of earshot.

"Yeah, but he's been a little weird lately."

"Lately?"

"Yeah, for the past few days. Touchy, I guess. Wound up real tight."

"Have you talked to him?"

"Tried to. He says he's fine, that— Hey, Dirk! Watch that front foot. You're opening your stance too much! Pay attention, will you?" Ed got up, muttering as he walked toward home plate. "If he'd get his mind out of beer cans..."

Everyone seemed to need his attention after that, and he was tied up until the victorious end of the game. The jubilant team gathered around Ed, clamoring about the apparently customary celebratory party.

"C'mon, coach, it has to be your place," the lanky pitcher whined, a rather sullen look on his face. "Rob says his place is out—his folks are having company tonight. And we gotta have a party."

"Okay, okay!" Ed threw up his hands in surrender. "But remember, Dirk, no booze and no fights. I don't need to be carting you off to the hospital again. And we're knocking off early—I have an early class tomorrow." He turned to Hunter hopefully. "Want to come with us?"

Hunter smiled, but shook her head. "I've got a couple of things I have to do tonight, but thanks anyway."

"Next time?"

"I don't know how long I'll be here, but maybe."

"Make it definitely." Ed grinned. "I'll walk you to your car."

Amid another chorus of whistles and catcalls, they crossed the grass to her car. Ed glanced over his shoulder at the team, who had grouped together into an obviously fascinated bunch of spectators. Then he looked back somewhat tentatively at Hunter, who read the look in his eyes easily.

"If you want a goodbye kiss to impress the troops, you've got the wrong lady," she said with a wry smile.

Ed had the grace to blush, but he was grinning. "Can't blame a guy for thinking."

"At least you admit it." She grinned back.

"How about a goodbye hug?"

"You're impossible," she laughed, but when he slipped an arm around her, she submitted to a brief embrace.

Ed pulled away as the roar of a motor split the silence. Both of them looked up as Rob Barrington leaned into a turn and raced out of the parking lot. Dirk, standing beside the open door of a battered, old, yellow Mustang, stared after him with a rather harsh expression Hunter couldn't read. She winced at the rising sound of Rob's bike, but her expression began to change as she looked thoughtfully after it.

"Wait till Dirk peels out of here," Ed said wryly. "He'll leave even more rubber than Rob did. He always does. That's why his car looks so thrashed."

"Boys will be boys." She laughed as she got into her borrowed Aliso Beach unmarked car.

"Next week," Ed called out to her as she pulled away, and she avoided a direct answer by merely waving. He was very nice, very charming and very handsome. And very, very young. Or seemed so to her, even though there was probably only three or four years difference in their ages. She sighed as she rounded the corner, but it was turned into a choked-off gasp as a battered pickup truck skidded to a halt directly in her path.

She hit the brakes, knowing that even if she hadn't been wrapped up in wondering about what she had just learned this afternoon, and what she wanted to check on as soon as she returned to the station, she wouldn't have been able to stop any sooner. The truck had come out of nowhere.

"Damn," she muttered as she got out to look at the scant six inches between her bumper and the truck's passenger door. When she saw who was stalking around the back of the vehicle, her eyes widened in surprise.

"Having fun?"

So much for peace, she thought as Josh's clipped, harsh words rang in her ears and his hostile stance made her own muscles tense. Wearily she gathered the edges of her temper, edges that seemed to fray so easily when he was around. "Nice truck," she commented mildly.

He looked taken aback for a moment. "What?" he snapped irritatedly.

"Your demolition derby vehicle?"

The piercing blue gaze narrowed, but he ignored her comment, saving his wrath for what had apparently been his original intent.

"Sam told me you were out there. Enjoy the game?"

Her eyebrows went up at his tone, but she answered as if he'd been sincere. "What I saw of it."

"I'm glad," he said scathingly, "even though you haven't done the first thing about finding my son."

Hunter studied him for a long moment. She knew what he'd said wasn't true; what's more, she knew that he knew it. Her green eyes looked him up and down, thinking in some oddly detached part of her mind that however attractive he was in the expensive clothes he wore to the office, he was devastating in tight, worn jeans and a snug T-shirt.

The unexpected battered, worn leather jacket he wore added just the slightest rough edge to his appearance and he looked like the tough young man who had thumbed his nose at the business world's hidebound traditions and done it his own way in spite of them. It's too bad, she mused, that he's lost that man along the way. I think I would have liked him.

"Well?" Her lack of response to his dig seemed to egg him on.

"I see," she said slowly. "It's fine if I take a break, as long as it's under your watchful eye." The green eyes went frosty as she looked at him, any warmth remaining from the night before fading before the sudden chill. "I have a suggestion, Mr. Kincaid. Since my manner of working is so unpleasant to you, I would recommend you stay in contact with Detective Singer regarding this case."

On those words, she was back in the car and wheeled it around the barricade of the truck with precise ease, leaving Josh staring after her. Furious that she had left before he'd been able to vent his anger completely, he raced to the driver's side of the truck and jumped in, intending to follow her.

By the time he got it started and out into traffic, she was out of sight, and he slammed a fist against the steering wheel in frustration. He hadn't been through with her, he thought, not by a long shot. Nobody talked to him like that, not even a cop.

He'd had enough, he told himself. Enough of her crazy methods, enough of the way she looked at him as if he was some new species she'd accidentally discovered. Hunter Garrett was impudent and cocky, he told himself with determined conviction. She had a hair-trigger wit and a temper to match.

Silently he ticked off the list of things that irritated him so much, smothering the little voice inside his head that was telling him that what he was calling impudence was merely the nerve to stand up to him, and cockiness, the knowledge of her abilities that he had praised that first day. And he absolutely refused to admit that his own reaction to her had anything to do with any of this.

I've had enough, he repeated under his breath, and today was the last straw. Damn right I'll talk to Singer from now on, he muttered viciously. Hanging around with that overgrown preppie coach. Letting him hang all over her. She should know better; she was too smart for that jerk. She could do a damn sight better.

Like you?

Fiercely he tried to shove the thought away, with all the others he'd been sidelining lately. It wouldn't shove. It just sat there, immovable behind his eyes, glowing brightly, jealously green.

Jealous? Him? He snorted scornfully. You couldn't be jealous unless you cared, and that was something he'd sworn off years ago. He didn't care about anyone except his son, he insisted silently. The only thing he felt for Hunter Garrett was irritation. Irritation and an infuriating desire he was determined to ignore. She brought out the absolute worst in him, and he didn't know what made him angrier—that he didn't know why, or that he couldn't seem to control it. He'd been able to control everything, until Hunter.

A cop who looked like the girl next door grown up into an incredible sexy woman, who quoted Mark Twain and poured her life into finding missing children, who had a temper to match the coppery highlights of her hair...

She was enough to madden anyone, he assured himself, and if the memory of that searing kiss, of holding her while she slept last night nibbled away at that certainty, he refused to admit it.

Hunter went over the list once more. She checked off item after item, compared the list to two other, shorter ones, and at last put them back on the desk with everything else. It wasn't proof, she thought, but maybe, just maybe, it was enough. It had better be, she muttered grimly to herself—I'm about out of time.

"Go for it?"

She looked up at Sam, who was sitting on the edge of the desk, and nodded, shrugging. "What have I got to lose?"

Sam laughed ruefully. "Just your shirt if old man Barrington decides to sue you."

"Only if I'm wrong."

"Okay. Let's go get him."

Hunter shook her head, and Sam looked at her questioningly. "Call your watch commander for me, will you? See if they can spare a uniform for a half an hour or so?"

"A patrol unit? Why do you—" Sam broke off as it came to him. "I get it. The full treatment, huh? Uniform, police car, the whole nine yards?"

Hunter nodded. "Every little bit helps. Maybe the ride here will take a tad of the starch out of young Mr. Barrington."

An hour later she was pacing the office, a little edgy in spite of the number of times she'd been through this. She glanced at the clock. She'd kept the impatient teenager cooling his heels for twenty minutes now; another five and she'd head for the interview room where he was waiting. With considerably less than patience, Sam informed her.

"Officer played it just right," he told her with a grin. "Wouldn't even talk to the kid, and brought him in past the jail. Opened his eyes a bit, I'd say. He's nervous as the boyfriend waiting to hear if the rabbit died."

"You have a flair for picturesque analogy, Sam," she said dryly. She gathered up several items from the desk, slid them into a folder and gave the detective a sideways look. "Let's hit it, Mr. Singer."

She followed him down the hall, and by agreement he waited outside the door while she went in alone. She ignored the young blonde in the room's only chair, walked around the table to stand behind it and put the folder down in front of her. She opened it, studied the contents for a moment, then shook her head slowly, as if in sad resignation.

At last she raised her eyes and fastened them unblinkingly on the young man. "Why, Rob?" she asked softly.

"I don't know what you're talking about," he answered sullenly, lowering his eyes.

Hunter sighed. She knew that whatever she did, nothing she got here could be used in a courtroom. He was a minor, he hadn't been arrested, hadn't been advised of his rights or any of the other things the courts had seen fit to require in order to protect the criminal. She didn't care. Her priority was where the law's should be, with the victim. As long as she got Jason Kincaid back alive, she would let the system do its best with the rest. Or its worst.

"You've still got a chance to come out pretty easy. But if you make us do it the hard way—"

"Am I under arrest, or what?"

"Not yet."

"Then you can't ask me questions," he said with an air of knowledgeable self-importance.

Another sidewalk lawyer, she thought tiredly. "You're a little confused, Rob. I can ask you anything I want if you haven't been arrested yet." I just can't use it to send you to jail, she added silently, wondering if perhaps she'd reached the saturation point with this crazy system that protected the bad guys and handcuffed the cops.

"Then I want a lawyer!"

She looked at him pityingly. "Why do you need a lawyer if, as you pointed out, you haven't been arrested?" He glared at her. "Look, Rob," she said reasonably, "you're not under arrest, and at this point I don't care if you ever are. I only want one thing, and you know what that is."

"Says who?"

"Says the evidence." She looked down, fingering the papers in the folder pointedly. For the first time, fear flashed across the tan, California-boy face.

"What evidence?"

"You're smart, Rob, but you didn't think it through." She raised her eyes to his suddenly. "When do your parents get home from New York, Rob? Why were you so worried about the team coming to your house that you lied about it?"

His lips thinned as he pressed them together. She watched him carefully as she casually added a seeming non sequitur. "Do you know where your mother gets her personal stationery, Rob?"

He paled, then went even whiter when she lifted the sealed-and-tagged plastic evidence bag that held the ransom note. Hunter felt that little thrill that always sent her blood racing when she knew she was on the right trail.

She held up a second tagged plastic bag, which held one of the letters from the ransom note. She knew she was gambling, taking a terrible chance that Rob would break here and now. If he didn't, he'd have all the time in the world to get rid of any traces of the evidence she was so generously telling him about.

"Do you know that paper from a single magazine can be matched with other paper from that same magazine? Like what might be caught in a pair of scissors?"

Rob shifted nervously in his chair, and she saw his knuckles whiten as he clutched at the arm. You'd better hope this works, Garrett, she told herself, because you're about out of ammo here, and you don't want to have to start bluffing.

She picked up a piece of paper from the open file and held it up so that he could see it was a copy of a police log, the log she'd found when the noisy blast of Rob's motorcycle at the ball field had sent her searching for anybody who might have complained about it.

"Did you know that there's a little old lady who lives across from the elementary school and is intensely irritated by the sound of a racing motorcycle, and never fails to call the police when she sees a certain bike racing past her house? Including the day Jason disappeared?"

"I didn't see him!" he insisted. His voice was considerably higher than it had been.

"So you said," Hunter said softly. "But strangely enough, that little old lady saw two people on that motorcycle that day. The same two she always saw."

He stared at her, his eyes now wide with fear, his jaw tight with strain. She held his gaze, but when he didn't speak, she let out a resigned sigh. "I'm sorry, Rob," she said gently. "It would have been so much easier." She gathered the bags and papers and slid them into the folder, closed it and began to walk toward the door.

"All right!"

Hunter was glad her back was to him when his shout rang out, so he couldn't see the relief that flooded her face. She controlled her expression, then turned back to face the young man, who had risen halfway out of the chair. Slowly she walked back, this time sitting on the edge of the table on the same side as the boy's chair.

She waited silently, and at last he began to talk.

Josh rubbed at weary, gritty eyes as he closed the file on his desk. He'd been scheduled for a series of conferences this week in Denver, but had told the airport representatives there that there was no way he could leave now. They had agreed, albeit grudgingly, to a telephone conference, and it had turned into a marathon session that had lasted until afternoon. He'd been going over the proposed changes for hours now, and darkness was filling the windows to his office, but nothing seemed to be registering on his numbed brain.

More than a week, he thought, feeling suddenly exhausted. He was beyond worry, beyond even panic, and only a stubborn endurance got him through each minute. He had little strength left to fight off an ever-growing sense of doom, and every hour that passed found that black, malignant cloud a little darker, a little lower. He stared at the phone, wondering if he should call home again. Maybe there had been a call. Or another note, more instructions.

In the act of reaching for the receiver, he stopped himself. If there was anything new, Sam Singer would let him know. Mrs. Elliott knew he was here; he'd told her this morning when he'd decided he couldn't stand just sitting at home waiting another minute. She'd refer Sam if he called.

Sam. The only one he'd talked to, in short, businesslike phrases that did nothing to alleviate the horror building inside him. He hadn't talked to Hunter since the day he'd cornered her at the ball field and she had told him to deal with Sam from now on. Well, he had, and only then had he realized how much of a release it had been just to talk to her.

She'd understood and more than once had found words to comfort where he'd thought no comfort was possible. That she knew exactly how he felt was a fact that had never been far from his mind since he'd learned about her son, and the admiration he felt for the way she'd chosen to deal with her own tragedy made those unexpected softer moments all the more poignant, and the moments when she incensed him all the more frustrating.

To his amazement, he found he missed those moments, as well. He missed seeing her round on him with green eyes flashing, that deadly wit drawn and ready, slicing deep with an edge that was sharpened with the truth more often than he cared to admit. She had made him look closely at himself, and if he didn't like what he saw, whose fault was it?

Forcing his eyes away from the tempting telephone, he found himself staring at the set of keys that rested beside it. The keys to the battered old pickup that now sat out in the parking lot. His demolition derby vehicle, he thought, his lips twisting in a wry smile.

He didn't know why he had felt the urge to drag out the old truck, and drive it, now of all times. It had been the first vehicle that Kincaid Industries had bought and paid for, and he'd never quite been able to bring himself to part with it. Cynthia had hated it, had even tried to sell it behind his back once, but he'd found out in time. Maybe that was part of it.

That it had become a symbol to him, both of where he'd begun and how far he'd come, he knew. What he didn't know was why, at this time of crisis in his life, he'd felt the overwhelming need to go back to it. Was it a need to go back to that time when life had been, not less painful, but less complex? Was it an attempt to return to the man he'd been then? It was something he'd wondered about since he'd found himself, without consciously making the decision, wearing the battered old leather jacket he'd virtually lived in during those days.

Or was it just that it made him feel closer to Jason? They had had some good times in that old truck; even as a toddler the boy had loved its rough ride. Josh could still hear his excited shrieks when they hit a bump.

Before he could stray down that worn path again, he pulled open the folder on his desk once more, trying to remember the time when this airport security system had been the most important thing in his life. It seemed a long time ago. He stared at the proposal before him, his handwritten notes from the conference call filling the margins at various places, and tried to concentrate on it.

He didn't know how much time had passed when his office door opened. He muttered in irritation. His secretary knew he wasn't to be interrupted; he didn't stop to think that she had gone home long ago. He looked up with sharp words on his lips, words that died unspoken when he saw Hunter standing there.

She looked lovely in a deep green silk shirt, which turned her eyes darkest emerald, and trim tan pants that accentuated her long legs. He knew he was staring, but he couldn't tear his eyes away. His blood began to pound in his ears, and he was suddenly warm.

He felt his body begin to respond, and he fought to call up that protective anger. He got to his feet, tossing down the pen he held, wondering why she was just standing there in the doorway. She wore an odd look of anticipation, a look he didn't understand.

"Have you ever heard of knocking?" he asked lightly.

Something came and went in the depths of the green eyes, something that made him feel a strange tightness in the pit of his stomach. When she spoke, her voice was even. And oddly soft.

"I thought my news might be a welcome interruption."

"What ne—" He broke off suddenly, and hope flared through him like wildfire. He opened his mouth to ask again, but he couldn't get the words out.

Hunter saw his effort, and smiled gently.

"It's over, Josh. I know where Jason is."

Chapter 7

"—hidden Jason ever since he'd gotten back and found him there. He said that if everyone hadn't thought it was a kidnapping, he never would have thought of a note."

Josh sat in the passenger seat of that innocuous unmarked car in numbed silence as Hunter explained. He couldn't quite believe it, couldn't absorb the fact that his hell was finally coming to an end.

"All Rob wanted was enough money to get away from his dad and never have to take anything from him again."

"He knew all the time where Jason was," Josh said shakily, stunned to realize that he had been within fifty feet of his son that day at the Barrington house.

Hunter nodded in the shadowed interior of the car. "I think, in his own screwed-up way, Rob was trying to help Jason."

"Help him?"

She nodded. "He said he and Jason were going to take off together. He figured you were just like his own dad and wouldn't care if your son dropped off the world. He said he knew how Jason felt and that he would have taken care of him."

Josh winced. "Better care, you mean."

"I think he saw himself in Jason, and striking out at you was like striking out at his own father. The idea of the money didn't come until later."

"'It's too late,'" he quoted softly, remembering the day she had told him what was wrong about that ransom note. He focused on her suddenly. "You sound like you feel sorry for Barrington."

She shrugged. "I just can't help thinking that maybe, a few years ago, he was just like Jason."

Josh recoiled, an immediate, automatic protest rising to his lips. But it was never uttered; he knew she was right.

"So you were right all along," he said finally, a little raggedly. "He hated it at home so much he ran away."

"Not exactly." She slowed down for a turn before going on, her tone gentle at the pain that had echoed in his voice. "When Rob picked him up that day, Jason knew they were leaving for Aspen and no one would be there. So he just hid, and stayed. He didn't really run away—"

"He just didn't want to come home."

"I know it's a fine point, but there is a difference."

"Some difference."

"Enough to be recognized by the court, if it had been a crime involved." She couldn't see him in the darkness of the car's interior, but she could feel his eyes on her, could sense his disbelief.

"It's what they call a crime of opportunity," she explained. "Something that under normal circumstances a person would never do, but when the right set of circumstances presents itself..."

"Yeah." Josh's tone was acid.

"Josh, stop. You've tortured yourself enough. It's over. That's all that matters right now."

Her words echoed in his head, and he felt the first little lightening of pressure, the first little flicker of relief penetrating the numbness. When they pulled up at a Stop sign lit by the golden halo of a streetlight, he glanced over at Hunter. She was smiling, a smile he'd never seen before.

It was a joyous smile, and Hunter knew it. She couldn't seem to help it anymore than she could understand it. She'd always felt relieved and happy at the end of a successful investigation, but never had she felt anything like this growing elation.

She could hardly wait to see that thousand-watt grin of Josh when he was free of the burden he'd been carrying, she thought, and if that was an unprofessional thought, so be it. There was no room for anything else in her heart right now. It bubbled up inside until, despite her efforts to smother it, the exultant smile slipped out.

To Josh it was irresistible. In that moment, looking at that smile, anything seemed possible. In a few minutes, he *would* see Jason.

Her joy was contagious, and he felt it begin to build in himself, sweeping all the pain and fear of the past week before it. God, he hadn't known how much he'd really missed her until now. He wanted to hug her. He wanted to kiss her breathless.... The sudden realization that he might now be free to do just that made his heart pound.

As if she'd heard the hammering sound of it, she turned to look at him. At his expression she drew in a quick little breath, her lips parting slightly. It was all the sign he needed, and in an instant he was across the bench seat. Heedless of quarters cramped by the steering wheel, he pulled her into his arms, his mouth darting down to hers with an eagerness he couldn't fight.

It was a joyous kiss, full of fire and light, heady with sheer relief. Hunter couldn't help but respond to it, not when his mouth was so ardent, his arms around her so strong, his exultation so evident. She kissed him back hungrily, not even stopping to wonder at herself. Only an impatient honk from behind them broke the spell. They jumped apart, Hunter staring at him.

"Sorry," Josh said as he slid hastily back across the seat. "I got carried away. Relief, I guess."

Right, Kincaid. Relief. That's all it is. And gratitude, maybe, for all the work she's done. That's all it's always been. Keep telling yourself that.

Hunter opened her mouth as if to answer him, then shut it again as if she didn't trust herself to speak. She nodded a little sharply, then, as another, louder honk sounded from behind him, turned her eyes forward and accelerated.

As she pulled into the long driveway of the Barrington house, Hunter could see the marked unit that had brought Rob Barrington back, and the familiar plain car that Sam Singer drove. Then, in the almost eerie glow of the outdoor lights that illuminated the front of the small pool house where Rob had admitted Jason had been hiding, she spotted Sam.

He was pacing. Nervously. A sudden chill pierced the warmth that had filled her. She slowed the car.

Rob Barrington was sitting on the edge of a low planter beside the open door to the guest house, his head down and cradled in his hands. The chill became a frost.

"Josh—"

She'd wanted to tell him to wait, but he was already out of the car before it had even come to a stop.

"Josh, wait."

He looked back over his shoulder at her, puzzled. Hunter nodded her head to one of the uniformed officers who stood to one side, and in answer to her unspoken command, he approached Josh.

"I need a couple of minutes first," she said to him, fighting to keep her rising dread from showing in her expression.

"But—"

"Please, Josh."

Something in her tone sent apprehension shivering along nerves that had thought they were through with fear.

"Hunter—"

"Just a couple of minutes."

Without giving him a chance to protest, she turned and headed for Sam. Josh took a step after her, but came up against a solid blue uniform.

"Please, Mr. Kincaid," the young man wearing it said politely. "It won't be long."

Something was wrong. He had seen it in Hunter's eyes and could sense it in the actions of Sam Singer and the dejected posture of Rob Barrington. A posture that changed rapidly as Hunter and Sam approached the teenager.

Rob leaped to his feet and gestured toward the open door of the pool house. His voice, squeakily adolescent in his distress, carried all too clearly to Josh.

"It's not my fault! He was here. I swear he was!"

Josh's blood turned to ice water in an instant. He ripped free of the young officer's grasp and headed for the agitated boy at a run.

"Josh—"

He ignored Hunter's outstretched arm. "What the hell is going on?"

Rob Barrington looked at Josh with fear vivid in his eyes. "Ho-honest," he stammered, "he was here. I never meant...all he wanted was to get away, I didn't—"

He broke off. Josh didn't move or speak, but Rob took a hasty step backward. And Hunter took a step forward.

"Josh, listen to me—"

He whirled on her. "Where is he?"

Hunter took a deep breath. "Josh, I'm sorry—"

"Is my son here or not?"

"No."

He stared at her for a long moment without breathing. Then he took in a deep gulp of air, and then another, like a man who'd had the wind knocked completely out of him. He looked around the brightly lit area as if he thought she was lying, as if Jason was hiding somewhere and this was all a bad joke.

"Josh, please, sit down for a minute." She gestured at one of the patio chairs. He ignored her. Or was too stunned to hear her. "Please," she repeated, putting a hand on his elbow to turn him toward the chair.

"No!" He twisted away from her and headed for the door of the small building. The officer standing guard moved to stop him, but Hunter shook her head and followed him into the pool house.

It consisted only of one large room and a bathroom. There was a refrigerator in one corner and on a table beside it a small hot plate. A few other tables, a phone, two chairs opposite a small television set and a daybed against one wall completed the furnishings. Posters of rock groups and surfers made up the decor. It was clearly a retreat for a teenager, not a guest room for the kind of people Robert Barrington Sr., ran with.

Hunter herded Josh toward one of the chairs. "Now sit down."

There was a snap of command in her voice that hadn't been there before, but it barely seemed to penetrate his shock.

"No, I—"

"Sit down. You're at a crime scene that has to be preserved."

That got through. "Crime scene?"

He had gone suddenly pale, but he was listening now.

"That's what we have to assume until we know different. Sit down, Josh."

She knew her voice was harsh, but she couldn't help it. She had violated a basic tent of police work by bringing Josh here before everything was resolved, and now it had blown up in her face. She had ignored common sense and procedure in her eagerness to end his torment, and in doing so had single-handedly raised and then destroyed his hopes. She had bent the rules because she had let herself become personally involved in this case, and she had no one to blame but herself. The knowledge ate at her like acid.

"Get Barrington in here." She didn't try to hide her anger; she knew it was at herself, but Rob didn't. She would use whatever tools she had now, and to hell with the consequences.

"I tell you, he was here!"

Rob was talking before he was even completely inside. Hunter didn't speak, just pointed at the daybed. He sat on the edge of it, casting a wary eye on Josh as he did so.

"I never meant for him to get hurt or anything—he was just

here, and I helped him! He could have gone home if he wanted, like I didn't lock him in or anything."

"I know that, Rob."

He looked startled as he stared at her.

"You...believe me?"

"I know you didn't mean to hurt him. But it won't matter much unless you help me now."

"But I don't know anything! He was here, now he's gone—that's all I know!"

"Calm down, Rob." She eyed him levelly. "Did Jason know about the note you sent?"

Rob sent another wary glance in Josh's direction.

"He won't hurt you, Rob. Just help us. Did Jason know?"

"No. I wouldn't tell the kid something like that. I just told him I was going to get enough money so we could—" He broke off, his gaze flicking warily to Josh.

"I know you don't want Jason hurt," she said encouragingly. "I know you thought you were helping him."

"I was. I know how he felt. My dad's just like—" At a sudden movement from Josh, his mouth slapped shut.

"Never mind. It doesn't matter now. The only thing that matters is where Jason is."

"I keep telling you I don't know! He was here, I saw him right before the cops came and got me."

"This afternoon?"

Rob nodded. "I took him some food from the house."

"Could he have seen the police car, maybe gotten scared?"

Rob shook his head. "No. They picked me up out at the gate. He couldn't have seen them."

"You were on your bike?"

"No. It's in the shop. I was waiting for Dirk to pick me up to go to practice, but the cops got here first."

Hunter considered this as she walked around the perimeter of the room. She paused by the hot plate, then looked back at Rob.

"Chili?"

"Yeah."

Josh's head came up and he spoke for the first time, in a flat, dull voice that was as lifeless as the look in his eyes. "Jason doesn't like chili."

Rob paled, but answered. "I know, but it was all I could find in a hurry."

Hunter turned to Josh. "Doesn't like it as in doesn't want it, or as in absolutely won't eat it?"

He shrugged, a weary, beaten gesture that knifed through a heart already lacerated with guilt. "Absolutely won't. At least the last I remember." He didn't even ask why it might matter.

"Well, somebody did."

She lifted the empty can out of a wastebasket by a tiny corner of the torn label and set it on the table next to the equally empty bowl, which held a spoon dirty with the remnants of the spicy meal.

"Did you open the can?" She switched her gaze back to Rob, who shook his head. She bent to the wastebasket again, rustled the contents for a moment, then straightened up.

Or started to. Her movements stopped abruptly, and she bent back down to pull the plastic container out from the wall. With her right little finger carefully through the pop ring, avoiding the half-crumpled sides, she lifted an empty beer can from the floor.

"Yours?" She held it up for Rob to see.

"No. I didn't keep any down here, not while Jase was here."

Hunter's eyebrows rose. "Looking out for his morals?"

Rob flushed. "He's just a kid. He didn't need to have beer around. It's probably left over from one of the team parties."

Hunter risked a glance at Josh; his brows were furrowed as if Rob's words had struck an unexpected note.

"That's it, Rob?" He nodded slowly, that frightened look lingering in his eyes. "Okay." She looked toward the officer at the door. "Take him out, will you, Jim? See if we can get in touch with his parents." Rob groaned but went without protest.

As soon as he was out the door, Sam came in. He ran a hand over his hair, cast a glance at Josh that was nearly as wary as Rob's, then looked at Hunter.

"I'd swear he was just as surprised as we were," he said.

Hunter nodded. "Put in a call for CSI, will you?" Sam nodded, then looked at Josh once more, a question in his eyes. "Give me a few minutes, will you?" Hunter said.

Sam left, pulling the door closed behind him, and Hunter knew he would keep everyone out until she opened it again. She crossed the room, pulled up the second chair in front of Josh and sat down. She had to swallow heavily before she could get out the words.

"I am so sorry, Josh. I never should have brought you here until I'd made sure."

Josh lifted his gaze to her face, and for the first time since he'd realized what had happened, something of life flickered in the steel blue depths. True, it was pain, but at least it was life. Hunter didn't know it was in response to her own expression, to the agony and guilt that were showing in her own face and eyes.

"Not your fault he ran away again," he muttered.

"But I should have been certain before I let you get your hopes up."

Her distress echoed in her voice. He knew in that moment that she was as devastated as he was. He looked at her for a long moment, and then, to her amazement, he lifted a hand and placed it over hers. When he spoke, the gruffness of his voice told her of the emotion he was holding in.

"I'm not sure it would have been any better to find out later that we were so close but still too late."

Hunter sat back, stunned. There were depths to this man she hadn't even guessed at. Now, when at the very least she had expected justified anger, he was soothing her guilt as no one else but the victim of her misjudgment could, and with a quiet compassion she was amazed he could summon up after what he'd been through. She watched as he rubbed his hand over his eyes, and wondered if he was just too spent to be angry.

"You believe Rob, then?" she asked quickly, unable to deal with the feelings that were tumbling around inside her.

"Yes. I'm not sure why, but I do."

"He's too scared to lie."

"That's part of it."

She studied his face for a moment. "What he said about the beer got to you, too, huh?"

If he hadn't been so devastated, the look he gave her would have been sheepish. Slowly he nodded. Then his expression changed to one of utter anguish, matched by the harsh undertone of his voice.

"He ran away again."

Hunter started to speak, then caught herself. Josh might have been plunged back into the depths of grief, but he didn't miss her sudden stop.

"What?"

She shook her head. She'd made one bad mistake tonight, she didn't want to make another.

"Hunter..."

She looked away, then nearly jumped at the shock that leaped through her when he reached out and turned her chin gently back to face him.

"Better dump it on me now," he said without a trace of sarcasm, "while I'm too numb to feel it."

"It's nothing."

His mouth twisted ruefully. "Nothing is ever 'nothing' with you."

"I just..." She stopped and looked around the room once more. "Why would he run from here? He had everything he needed—food, shelter and Rob to help."

Josh made a strangled little sound as he stared down at his hands. "Why would he run indeed? All the comforts of home..."

"I'm sorry, Josh. I didn't mean to—"

"Don't bother trying to spare my feelings. I'm not sure I have any left."

You do, she thought. You've just had them in cold storage for so long you don't recognize them anymore. After a long moment he raised his head to look at her, a world of weariness and despair clouding his eyes.

"What now?"

"We start over," she said grimly, pulling a notepad out of the pocket of the jacket behind him.

Josh slumped in the chair. What did you expect, he told himself bitterly, some kind of miracle? Yes, some little voice inside rose up to answer. You expected Hunter Garrett to pull off exactly that.

And she would have, he thought, if only Jason had waited a little longer. Or if Rob Barrington had crumbled a little sooner. If, if, if. And if he hadn't let his son slip so far away, none of this would have ever happened. Things would have gone on peacefully, undisturbed.

And he never would have met Hunter Garrett. He was surprised at the strength of the regret that one thought caused.

"Hunter?" Sam's voice was muffled through the door. "CSI's here."

Josh looked at her as she stuffed her notes back in her pocket. "CSI?"

"Crime Scene Investigation." He winced, but recovered quickly. He was regaining control, she thought. "Fingerprints, evidence, that kind of thing," she elaborated. He nodded dully. She went to open the door.

"I want the room dusted, especially those cans and the silverware," she told the officer who came in with his case of equipment the size of a tackle box. "And a saliva typing on the spoon and the beer that's left in the can. We've got prints on Barrington at the station, so we can use those to eliminate his. We'll have to presume any child-size ones are Jason's, since we don't have any way to prove otherwise."

The man nodded and without a word began to dig into his case for the clinging black powder commonly known as "dust." Hunter watched him for a moment, then began another circuit of the room. Her eyes darted over every surface, probed into every corner.

She lifted the pillow on the daybed, checked under and among the folds of the blanket at its foot. She thumbed through the stack of worn surfing magazines and smaller pile of comic books on the small table next to the bed. She checked over, under and behind every single item in the room.

Josh watched her with a weariness that seemed to increase even as he looked. The reaction was setting in fiercely now, the plunge to the depths after the pinnacle of hope, and he wondered how she found the strength. She had been as high as he had; he had seen that in her smile in the car, had felt it when he'd kissed her. She had fallen as far as he had when she'd realized something was wrong; he'd seen that in her eyes.

The only sign that she was anything less than calm was a compressed sigh that escaped as she dropped down on the edge of the daybed where Rob had sat. The movement of the mattress jostled the night table, and something rolled off onto the floor from beneath the stack of comic books.

Hunter leaned down to pick it up, reached out to put it back on the table, then stopped. She looked at it for a moment, then rose and walked back across the room to kneel beside the chair.

"Josh?"

He raised his head from where it was cradled wearily in his hands.

"When was the last time you saw Jason write something?"

He looked at her blankly. "What?"

"Have you seen him write anything in—" she paused for a second, thinking "—the last six months?"

He let out a breath. "I suppose so. I don't remember. Math homework, maybe."

"Did he chew on his pencil?"

He gaped at her. "What the hell has—"

"Did he? Because," she said slowly, holding out her hand, "I need to know if I should start looking for something he might have written with this."

Josh stared at the small stub of a pencil that was cradled in the palm of her slender hand. The eraser was worn down to the edge of the metal holder, and the yellow barrel was marked with several small, even indentations. Teeth marks. Small teeth marks.

A sudden vision flashed through his mind. Jason bent over his homework at the kitchen table, having long ago ceased to dare to use his father's desk. Bent over a sheet of math problems with youthful intensity. With a bright yellow pencil between his teeth.

"Yes. Yes, he did. Does."

His conscious correction and the look in his eyes when he did it, tore at Hunter's already bruised emotions. She was trying to control her reaction, and his strained question caught her off guard.

"Couldn't you just have told me why you wanted to know? Or does that take away from the Garrett mystique?"

His accusation stung her raw nerves in a way she'd never felt before. She stood still, staring at him for a moment. Her first reaction was to think that it only hurt because she'd let him get too close. She'd let herself become too involved emotionally with this case. With him. She needed to back off. She backed up a step physically, as if she wasn't certain she could do it emotionally.

"Do you want to help look, or wait outside?"

There wasn't the slightest indication in her voice that she'd even heard his question. She sounded stiff and remotely chilly.

"I'll help." His voice echoed hers in coolness.

Deciding to start where she had found the pencil, Hunter handed him the stack of surfing magazines while she sat down with the comics in her lap.

These guys are nuts, he thought as he began to thumb through the pages of the third magazine. He stared for a moment at a two-page spread of a surfer in an impossible position under the over-hanging curl of an impossible wave of impossibly clear water.

It was then, when his own movements had stopped, that he realized that the rustling of pages across from him had also halted. He looked up instinctively, then stiffened.

Hunter wore an expression he'd only seen once before, on a moonlit night when she had handed him the little story that had torn his world apart.

"Hunter?" He could barely get it out.

Her head lifted, and he saw the unmistakable sheen of tears in the emerald eyes. His blood turned icy for the second time in this night's nightmare. Wordlessly she handed him a torn piece of notebook paper with a few penciled lines in Jason's careful scrawl.

Dear Daddy,

I know you're probly mad at me, but I promise I'll be real good and won't get in your way. And try real hard not to make you mad. I don't like it here anymore and I want to come home.

Jason

Josh read it through eyes that had begun to sting the moment he recognized the childish writing. By the time he'd finished it, he couldn't see anything through the blur of moisture. I *won't get in your way....*

God, how long had Jason thought of him like that, as some not-so-benevolent despot who was to be placated and feared? If only he'd taken more time, if only he hadn't let himself get so wrapped up in his work, if—

Don't drown in the "if only's." Hunter's words rose up in his mind, rescuing him from that yawning pit of guilt as they had before. You won't do Jason any good if you fall apart. She'd said something like that to him, too. It seemed, he realized suddenly, as if he had known her forever. And in a sense it was true; he'd lived a lifetime since he'd met her.

He sat staring at the note in his hand, only now realizing that he had nearly crumpled it in his despair. And only now did that one, small but potent phrase leap out to give him some small comfort. *I want to come home.* In spite of everything, Jason had wanted to come home.

He lifted his head to look at Hunter, a question leaping to his lips. He bit it back, just as he tried to hold back the brilliant flare of hope that was trying to rise within him. He wanted to ask but couldn't seem to form the words. Then her eyes met his, and his hesitation dissolved. He could ask her anything when she looked at him like that, without that impenetrable professional screen between them. He held up the note.

"Do you think he...might have gone home?"

Hunter saw the hope and that he was trying to fight it. You taught him well, she thought with a sudden flash of bitterness.

"Maybe," she said a little unsteadily. She glanced over her shoulder to where the CSI officer was sealing up the two cans and the spoon in plastic evidence bags. "Are you done with the phone?"

The officer nodded. "Nothing clear on it, except the little boy's."

Josh looked up sharply. Jason had used the phone? To call who? Surely any of his friends would have told if they'd heard from him? His eyes flicked to Hunter. He could almost see her brain racing. She got to her feet and headed for the phone, then stopped. She looked back at Jason.

"Call home first," she said softly.

He wasn't sure what she meant by first, but he nodded and got up out of the chair he felt he'd been in for hours. He crossed the room to the phone by the door and reached out for the receiver. He could see the traces of the sooty looking powder that was the fingerprint dust on it, and swallowed heavily as he realized that the last person who had picked it up could very well have been Jason.

"Josh?"

He turned to look at her.

"Why don't you just let Mrs. Elliott talk for a bit. If he's there, you know she'll say so. If she doesn't...just tell her I want to ask her something."

His brow furrowed, then cleared. "So she won't get her hopes up?"

"Yes." As you did, thanks to me.

Josh studied her for a moment, and Hunter had the oddest feeling that he knew exactly what she was thinking. Then he nodded, and Hunter had to look away from the sudden warmth that glowed in his eyes.

She knew from watching his face as he listened that Jason had not gone home. She hadn't thought that he had, but she hadn't wanted to dwell on what she did think, not yet. And most of all she didn't want to be the one to break the news to Josh. That knowledge ate at her; never in her life had she avoided the more unpleasant aspects of her work, even when she would have preferred to. But with Josh, she seemed to have suddenly developed a tendency to throw her rules out the window.

"—wants to ask you something."

Josh's voice was flat as he handed her the receiver, his face impassive. She kept her voice even as she spoke to the slightly puzzled older woman.

"Have you been getting any odd phone calls at the house, Mrs. Elliott?"

She felt Josh stiffen beside her, but he stayed silent as she listened to the answer.

"No, I'm afraid not." There was a pause. "Yes, he's all right. Amazingly so. Thank you, Mrs. Elliott." She hung up.

Of all the questions that were spinning in Josh's mind, he could only seem to ask one.

"Who's amazingly all right?"

She met his eyes steadily, and there was an echo of his own earlier warmth in the luminous green.

"You are. She's worried about you." She said it quietly, her eyes betraying that Mrs. Elliott wasn't alone in her concern.

He didn't understand why he'd asked, and he surely didn't understand why her answer took his breath away. She held his gaze for a moment, and it stunned him to realize how much he treasured those moments when she let down that businesslike defense.

Defense? What an odd word to think of, he thought. Was it true? Was that cool, professional demeanor part of a formidable defense system? Lord knows, after what he'd learned about her, he couldn't blame her in the least. He'd never thought of a woman in terms of courage, until Hunter. He couldn't help but think of her that way.

She was looking at him rather oddly now, and he yanked his wandering mind back to the situation at hand.

"Do you really think he called home?"

She shrugged. "Somebody has." His eyebrows shot up. "Mrs. Elliott said there have been several hang-up calls on the answering machine when she's checked it. She erased them because she didn't want to upset you any—Josh?" He had gone suddenly pale.

"I...there've been calls at my office, too. My secretary thought it was just a prank...."

Hunter grabbed the phone and quickly dialed.

"This is Investigator Garrett. I need you to contact phone company security, ASAP. I need an advance toll check." She read the number off the sticker below the number pad. "I want every number that was called from this phone in the last week, and I want it yesterday." She paused, listening for a moment before she went on impatiently. "Yes, I know it usually takes days. And I know they charge for each number. I'm only looking for two."

Josh listened as she recited both his home and office numbers.

By the time the rest of the pool house had been gone over with the proverbial fine-toothed comb, it was well after midnight. Wearily Hunter and Josh sat in her car preparing to leave.

"—could get a search warrant for the house," she was saying, "but I believe Rob when he says Jason was never there."

"Then it would be a waste of time, wouldn't it." Josh's words were not a question.

Hunter sighed. "I'm sorry, Josh," she said softly. "If I'd been a little quicker—"

"No." He cut her off, speaking with a calm that seemed extraordinary to her under the circumstances. "If there's any blame here, it's mine. Jason ran away because of me. We wouldn't be here at all if it wasn't for that."

No, Hunter agreed silently. And I would never have known Josh Kincaid existed. The thought made her feel strangely downcast.

"So what do we do now? Do you have any...feeling about this?"

Hunter stared at him. Just when she would have expected him to fall apart, he seemed to have found a new reservoir of steely strength. And despite his early jibe about her methods, he was asking her about the "feelings" he had scoffed at before, with all appearances of taking them with deadly seriousness. Did she really know this man at all?

"Yes," she began slowly, "but..."

"But what?"

"You won't like it."

His mouth twitched. "I never noticed that stopping you before."

"All right," she retorted, stung once more for a reason she didn't understand. "I don't think Jason ran away from here."

Josh sighed when she ended it there. "I presume you're going to eventually tell me—"

"Because," she jumped in before he could finish, "he had all he needed here. Because that note, and those calls say he wanted to come home. Because he wouldn't have left without telling Rob. And because I...I *feel* it."

She looked at him, almost glared, waiting for him to make another derogatory comment about her "feelings."

"I never questioned that. What I was about to ask was if you had any idea what *did* happen."

He spoke so evenly, so calmly, that Hunter felt her anger deflate like a balloon that had just been pricked by a needle. She was at a total loss. Never had she felt so compelled to defend her work, her methods, nor had she ever been so touchy about the topic. And never, ever did she explain it.

The Hunter Garrett mystique?

His words echoed in her head, slicing, stinging. God, had she really—

"No," she said aloud, in response to her own thoughts, then hastily changed it to fit his question. "No, I don't. I just know that this time it feels real."

Josh had dreaded that answer, even as he had half expected it. "You don't think that Rob just moved him? To make sure he didn't get caught?"

She hesitated, not certain how resolute this new calm of his was.

"I don't, either," he said, accurately reading her silence. "Like you said, he was too scared to lie."

Hunter nodded.

"Then it's a whole new ball game, isn't it?"

"I'm afraid so."

She reached for the ignition and started the car, the sudden revving of the engine the only outward sign of her frustration.

Chapter 8

Jason had wanted to come home. Josh was amazed at how much comfort, how much strength that tiny bit of knowledge gave him.

"He wanted to come home," he said softly, almost to himself.

Hunter lifted her head to look at him. Although he still carried the marks of the past week in the lines grooving his face and the weariness of the blue eyes, he seemed somehow less tense, stretched a little less tautly.

"Yes," she agreed quietly, "he did."

They were sitting in Victor Curtis's office, a lonely cell of light in the darkened police station. She picked up her pen, made another quick note on the pad in front of her, then tossed it down with barely controlled impatience. Josh raised an eyebrow at her. She let out an exasperated sigh.

"I want to get started now, not when it's convenient for the rest of the world," she grumbled. "But I've found people to be less than cooperative when you wake them up at four in the morning."

"You mean not everyone is up now?" he asked wryly.

Hunter shot a quick, startled look at him. She'd been right; there was something different about him, some change that she couldn't put her finger on, but knew was there as surely as she knew her own name. If she thought it odd that she should be so certain about the unspoken feelings of a man she'd known for such a short time, she didn't dwell on it. She didn't want to dwell on it; it made her edgy, and she couldn't afford that right now.

She turned her attention back to the growing list of things she planned to do as soon as morning—the normal world's morning—arrived. She would do the door-to-door this time, she thought, and Sam could—

"Nobody knew he was there except Rob."

Josh's quiet words, words that cut straight to the central point around which all other thoughts had been whirling, stopped her train of thought abruptly. She looked up at him once more and nodded.

"Then how...?"

"I don't know."

"If only Rob knew he was there, how could who- ever...took him have known? He couldn't have just stumbled across him."

"Coincidences do happen."

"That big of a coincidence? You don't believe that."

"No."

"What, then?"

The possibilities had been percolating in her mind for hours now, ever since her heart had plummeted to her feet outside the Barrington's guest house.

"Perhaps Jason got bored, went outside and was seen. Or Rob let something slip that he doesn't remember, or won't cop out to. Or maybe Jason really did start home, and something happened on the way. With those flyers plastered all over the county now, anybody could have recognized him. And realized you were willing—and able—to pay to get him back, be it reward or by inference, ransom."

She'd been thinking out loud, and realized with a sudden shock that she had never meant to speak those words. God, why did she always seem to do this around him? She said things she never had before, told him things she never meant to. And even more disturbing, she seemed to have a great deal of trouble hanging on to the cloak of professionalism that she had spent so many years developing.

She turned stricken eyes to Josh, but he was looking at her levelly, his equanimity apparently intact.

"You're...taking this awfully well." Her voice was penitent, apologizing silently for parading the possible horrors before him.

Something flickered in the tired blue eyes, as if he'd heard her unspoken words as well as her spoken ones. "So are you," he said softly. "All that work... But at least you know you were right."

She swallowed tightly. "That doesn't get Jason back home." Her gruff tone hid her emotion at his generous words, but oddly he looked as if he knew that, too. She didn't understand what had happened, or why; she only knew that she was seeing the real Josh Kincaid, that somewhere he had found once more the strength that had built his empire. It was a strength that both awed her and attracted her; the combination frightened her.

She got suddenly to her feet, gathering her things.

"What?" He looked at her quizzically.

"I'm going to go back to the Barrington house. Maybe I missed something."

"Hunter, you went over every inch of that place. Twice."

She dropped her keys onto the desk as she expelled a long breath. "Then I'll go talk to Rob again. Maybe he'll remember something."

"You spent three hours with him going over every minute of the last two weeks."

"So we'll go over it again."

Josh hadn't moved out of the chair he'd dropped into when they'd got here. He looked up at her, at the stubbornly defiant set of her chin and the determined glow in weary, reddened eyes. His heart seemed to twist inside him. God, she had more spirit than anyone he'd ever known. And he knew suddenly that that was what set her apart from other women who might be more traditionally beautiful, that it was that valiant spirit shining through that made her so different, so special.

Somewhere deep inside him a warning bell went off. He drew himself up in the chair, disturbed. Never had he been so aware of what lay beneath the surface of a woman, especially an attractive one. Cynthia had taught him brutally that there was nothing behind the lovely facade, and he hadn't looked for or expected anything different since her death.

He didn't want anything different, he told himself, ignoring the hint of desperation that suddenly echoed in that inner voice. It was only when you were fool enough to expect love, to believe that facade was real, that you got into trouble.

So why, then, was he so certain that there wasn't an ounce of facade to Hunter Garrett? And why did it scare the hell out of him?

He didn't know, and didn't want to know, not now. He got hastily to his feet.

"I have a better idea. Let's get something to eat. I'm starved."

He wasn't—he hadn't really had an appetite for days on end—

but she looked so tired yet so determined to go on in spite of it, that all he wanted to do was make her sit down and rest, at least for a while.

It was a fiercely protective feeling, one he'd never felt for anyone except Jason, and he wasn't at all comfortable with it. Not to mention that she didn't need his protection at all. What she needed was protection *from* him, that little inner voice piped up, and it was all he could do not to blush, he who had lost that ability, or so he'd thought, when he was ten and his father had humiliated him in front of his entire fifth-grade class.

He'd sworn then, when his father had arrived to drag him out of the class for daring to wear those "grubby" blue jeans instead of the pressed slacks the kids always laughed at, that he'd never let anything embarrass him like that again. Yet there he was, coloring like a school kid all over again.

"You must be hungry, too," he said defensively when he saw her staring at him. "And you said there wasn't much you could do until morning."

"Yes, but..." She faltered, her already raw emotions confused by the odd look in his eyes.

Josh read her expression with an ease he'd never known with anyone before, and he wondered when he'd acquired it. Or learned it. He didn't wonder from whom.

"Don't," he said softly. "It's not your fault."

She looked startled, and Josh was honest enough to admit he enjoyed being on the other end of the surprise for a change. When she finally spoke, her voice was desolate, barely above a whisper.

"I should have guessed sooner."

Josh's throat tightened. You would think it was her own son, he thought. A ripple of feeling swept through him, so fierce and new and unexpected that he couldn't put a name to it. But his scarred, barricaded heart knew what it was, and hastened to protect itself. Every case is special to her, it told him—she said so herself. He tried to listen, knew he had to, but it was so hard when he wanted to—

"We were so close."

He couldn't do it. The quiet misery in her voice drowned out his heart's warning more effectively than a roll of thunder. Convulsively he reached for her, feeling the lightning for that thunder go racing along his nerves at the feel of her shoulders, slender and warm, beneath his hands.

Before she realized what was happening, she was in his arms, and by then it was much too late. It felt so good; he was so warm, so strong, surely it couldn't hurt, just for a minute....

She heard the steady thud of his heart as her cheek was pressed to his chest, and felt a button digging into her skin. She meant to lift her head away then, but instead found herself only shifting so she could avoid the button. It became a tiny, snuggling movement, certainly nothing to cause Josh to suck in that sudden, sharp breath.

And why, she wondered, had the thud of his heart quickened beneath her ear? Why, when she felt so wonderfully sheltered, did he seem suddenly tense?

He moved then, slowly, and had it not seemed so impossible, she would have sworn his lips had brushed over her hair. Just the thought made her pulse accelerate, and a hot, vivid memory of that kiss in the gazebo seared her mind.

She pulled away hastily, color flooding her cheeks. Josh's eyes were fastened on her, and his lips slightly parted as if he, too, had suddenly found the room short of air.

"I..."

Whatever she'd been about to say died away when she lifted her head to meet his gaze. How could eyes the color of a blue iceberg be so hot? She tried to pull away, but his arms were tight around her.

"I know," he whispered, "it's crazy, but..."

She saw the pulse beating in his throat as he lowered his head. His lips parted hers gently, his tongue flicking over her as his fingers threaded through the burnished warmth of her hair. He tilted her head back to deepen the kiss, and suddenly she knew how those iceberg blue eyes could burn so intensely; it made as much sense as what he did to every bone in her body.

His tongue probed, tasted, and she met it with her own in an erotic dance. It seemed to be the only thing she could do; the rest of her body refused to listen to her mind's demand to move away. The warnings that normally clamored in her head were distant and dim, muffled by the hot, pleasurable fog that had enveloped her.

She moaned against his lips; he made a small sound and pressed her closer. Clothing was a puny barrier against his heat, and she felt her breasts, crushed against his chest, swell and rise to it. She could no more stop the sinuous movement as she rubbed against him than she could stand on her own when he was kissing her so thoroughly, so deeply.

Josh's hands slid over the silk of her blouse, thinking that it was coarse compared to the living silk beneath. She twisted in his arms again, and as if of their own will, his hands slipped down to the full curve of her breasts, cupping and lifting their soft, feminine weight. He heard her sharp intake of breath.

"Josh!"

She sounded almost frightened, and it was enough for him to regain a grip on his rapidly slipping control. He wrenched his mouth from hers.

"Let's get out of here," he said raggedly.

She stared up at him, green eyes looking a little dazed. "What?" she whispered.

He groaned. "Before that couch over there gets too tempting to resist."

Color flooded her face, and she looked around as if only now remembering where they were. Or only now realizing what had happened.

"May—maybe food is a good idea," she stammered, avoiding looking at him.

"Yeah." It came out low and harsh, and her color deepened.

Within a half hour Hunter was sitting in the booth at Chuck's Burgers, her arms wrapped around herself as if she were afraid of flying apart. It was the only outward sign of her inner turmoil; years of training had schooled her to keep it out of her face, and she kept her eyes lowered.

She didn't understand, and it frightened her. Mere hours ago she had been censuring herself for becoming too involved in this case, for letting her emotions draw her too close to the man who should be strictly business, and then she had gone straight into his arms like a moth with an incurable passion for the flame that will spell its doom.

Her emotions, she thought in bewilderment. What on earth were they? How could you identify feelings you'd never experienced before? She had felt certain with Dan, before. He had been kind then, and caring, and she had been comfortable and secure. She had wondered occasionally if there was more, if she was missing something, but it had been enough. Then.

Josh had made her feel secure, she thought, but knew as soon as the word formed in her mind that it was a poor, inadequate description of what she'd felt, huddled in his embrace. She'd felt safe, protected somehow, as if she'd found a sheltered harbor after a long, hard storm.

But comfortable? Hardly. What Josh Kincaid made her feel was far from comfortable. No one had ever been able to make her so furious so fast, or played such havoc with her equilibrium. Or her senses. Oh, yes, let's not forget that, the way his slightest touch sent flickers of heat racing along nerves that had been asleep for years, the way his kisses charred to ashes her ideas of her own ability to respond. Yes, she ordered herself, let's forget that.

A sudden realization made her pale in shock. Was she really sitting here assessing how Josh Kincaid made her feel as if he occupied a place in her life comparable to Dan? She barely stopped herself from looking at him with all her confusion in her eyes, and color slowly stained the paleness of her face.

Josh would have given a great deal to know what had caused the chain of expressions that flitted across her fine-drawn features. He wasn't stunned by the realization this time, even though it had been many long years since he'd cared anything about a woman's thoughts or emotions. He sighed, resignation warring with apprehension; he'd been charting new territory since the moment he'd met Hunter Garrett, and this was no exception.

Hunter stared across the small table at him. Who was this Josh, this man who had somewhere in the worst depths of his tragedy, found sudden strength? A memory flooded her mind, of Dan after Timmy's funeral, a broken and battered man who had struck out at anyone and everyone, even the people who loved him and tried to help him the most. She had waited patiently for him to come out of it, longing for someone to share her grief with. He never did.

She had seen the same signs in Josh Kincaid, although he had never lost control like Dan, nor had he resorted to the false solace of alcohol. But, she realized now with a little shock, never had she thought he would wind up as Dan had. Somehow she had known that there was too much strength at the core of this man, however misguided it might have been in the beginning.

"Your food's getting cold," she said abruptly, only now realizing that the full plates had been sitting on the table for several minutes.

His head came up at her words, and he looked pointedly at her own untouched meal.

"Okay, mine is, too."

"That's because food isn't what we wanted."

He moved his arm as if to reach for her hand, then stopped suddenly, curling his fingers in on themselves as he drew back. Hunter saw the movement and silently thanked him. She wasn't up to dealing with what his touch did to her right at the moment.

She looked up then, dreading it yet knowing she couldn't avoid meeting his eyes any longer. The only thing she saw in the blue depths was a turmoil to match her own. She took a quick, deep breath. It had never occurred to her that he might be feeling the same thing, that his drawing back from her had been for his own protection, not hers.

Don't be an idiot, Garrett, she told herself sharply. You're jumping to conclusions based on nothing but a few kisses shared under stress. That's all it was, all it had ever been. It had to be. Anything else was impossible. And improbable, she added ruefully. But hopefully not incurable, because she couldn't deal with these foolish yearnings and wayward thoughts much longer.

Color began to rise in her cheeks again, and she had to lower her eyes to her still-untouched meal. Some poker face you are, she muttered silently. A cop who can't keep a straight face isn't worth much.

She made herself eat, wondering at how something that had been so good when she'd been here before could be so tasteless now. She was aware of Josh taking regular, methodical bites, as if eating was some unwanted but necessary routine that had to be completed to enable him to keep going.

In his effort to keep his eyes off her, Josh was concentrating intently on the meal he didn't really want. But he couldn't get out of his mind the look that had been in her eyes when he had made himself not touch her. It had been gratitude, he told himself sourly, gratitude that he'd left her alone. It hadn't been longing he had seen in the green depths, and he couldn't kid himself that it was.

And it was just as well, he said to himself firmly, chewing systematically on a French fry he barely tasted. He had no room in his life for that kind of complication, hadn't had even before Jason had disappeared.

Jason. He stopped in the act of reaching for another fry. He waited, waited for the flood of self-contempt, waited for the overpowering anguish and misery to fill him once more. It didn't come. His grief was just as strong, just as painful, but it was different somehow. The feeling of loathing for what he had let happen had been reduced to a pang of regret that he knew instinctively would last for a long time, but it no longer crippled him with its strength.

He was still pondering the change as she drove him back to his office. He looked over at her, studying her face. In profile, she was backlit by the glow of the street lamp they were passing, giving her an ethereal look that tugged at something deep inside him. He knew that she had shown him the way out of that overwhelming morass of guilt, and he wished he could find the words to thank her. But he had made certain he owed no one anything for so long that thanks was something he'd forgotten how to give.

Hunter could see the Kincaid Industries building several blocks before they got there. In a large complex close to the small but busy John Wayne Airport, the bronzed-glass building caught the first rays of dawn and sent them flying.

It was the sight of that now-familiar building that sent her mind racing back to that morning a few days ago when Sam Singer had tossed a two-month-old local news magazine on her borrowed desk.

"I thought you might be interested," he'd said casually.

It had seemed innocuous enough, folded open atop the pile of messages, notes and file folders, and she'd picked it up to look at the article Sam had obviously meant her to see.

She had glanced at the attention-getting, gruesome photo of an airliner destroyed by a terrorist bomb, with its caption heralding the Eureka II, then at the lead paragraph of the article beneath it:

> John Jay Chapman once said that 'it is unquestionably possible for an incorruptible man to succeed in business. But his scruples are an embarrassment. He must make up in ability what he lacks in moral obliquity.' In today's business world, there is no clearer example than Josh Kincaid. A man of the highest scruples, who makes even the strongest of the power players play by his rules, he has taken his company to the top by dint of sheer, unbridled ability and plain hard work.

She'd known that, she'd thought as she had turned the page. Not from any reading or research she'd done, or from what she'd been told, but from knowing the man herself. He would be incapable of any less.

She'd stared down at the photograph on the page she had just turned. It was Josh, years before, at the ground breaking for the building that now housed his offices. Young, vital and looking a little bit wild, his dark hair a bit shaggy and tossed by the breeze, he wielded the shovel like a man who knew how to use it. He looked so unshadowed, she'd thought, realizing how haunted he'd been by comparison since she'd known him.

She'd recognized the leather jacket he wore, looking newer and less battered in the photo. The look in his eyes, no less piercing because the picture was in black and white, was almost fierce. He looked like he could build the whole thing himself if he had to, and would if anyone got in his way.

She hadn't seen that look from him, she thought as she pulled into the deserted parking lot. Not until last night, when a trace of it, an echo of that fierce fire, had shone in the steely blue eyes. It was part of the difference she'd seen in him, showing her his tension had not lessened but merely changed. She wondered what it meant.

They had reached the lane that led to the doors of the building, and she looked at him questioningly.

"My truck's over there." He gestured toward the battered vehicle parked a surprising distance from the building.

"I would have thought the chairman would have his own parking place," she said as she maneuvered the car in that direction.

"I need the walk. Besides, if I parked that thing in my spot, they'd probably tow it away."

A joke? Had he really made a joke? She stared at him for a moment; the twitch at the corner of his mouth made it unmistakable. There had been, she thought, more to this change than she realized. What on earth had done it? After a moment she spoke again.

"It's...special to you somehow, isn't it?"

He looked at her sharply, but was unable to read her expression in the shadowy interior of the car. "Haven't lost your touch, I see," he said wryly.

"Let's just say I find the timing rather indicative," she said carefully, hoping they weren't going to argue again.

He was silent for a moment, and Hunter thought he wasn't going to answer at all.

"It is special, I guess," he said at last. "It was the first company car for Kincaid Industries. And I thought it proved something."

"To who?"

Josh's mouth twisted wryly. Anyone else would have asked what it had proved; leave it to Hunter to see through to the real core.

"To my father, mostly." He couldn't believe he'd said it; he never spoke of this to anyone.

Hunter waited. The few brief mentions he'd ever made of his parents had left her with the impression that they were hardly close, and she hadn't forgotten his words about them the first time they'd met.

"Did you prove it?" she finally asked.

"Not to him."

His flat tone startled her. "But—"

Josh let out a long, harsh breath that cut her off. "My father is a sour, bitter old man, and to him I'm a worthless bum. And my mother agrees with everything he says, because it saves her the trouble of forming an opinion of her own."

Hunter stared at him in disbelief. "He can't think that now?"

Josh shrugged. "He's thought it for as long as I can remember. It's all I ever heard, growing up." His mouth twisted into what could have been a smile. "I walked out when I was sixteen. Figured I'd better find out if they were right." He shrugged again, as if the miracle he'd accomplished since then was nothing at all.

"But how can he still—?"

"He does."

He reached for the door handle and yanked it. He got out in one swift movement. Hunter got out, too, and followed him over to the pickup. She looked up at the building that soared above them.

"Then he's a fool," she said softly.

"Yes."

"And it still matters to you, doesn't it? That he won't admit he was wrong?"

"Only when I let it."

He reached in his pocket and tugged out a small ring of keys. He was aware of her silence and he unlocked the door, but he was still too stunned that he had talked of this forbidden subject to react.

"Josh?"

He pulled the door open, then turned to face her. She looked fragile and weary in the early-morning light. "What?"

She glanced up at the building once more, then back at him. "Would any of this exist if you hadn't had something to prove to him?"

He stiffened, staring at her. She feared she had gone too far, but refused to avoid his eyes. Gradually he relaxed, and finally she saw the line of his mouth soften.

"You don't miss much about anything, do you?" He let out a short chuckle. "I guess I owe him for that, don't I?"

"You don't owe him anything. Today he'd be considered a child abuser."

Josh's eyebrows shot up. "He never—"

"Beat you? You think only blows hurt?"

He told himself it wasn't personal, that she was speaking generally, but her voice was so passionate, her eyes flashing a fire that made his nerves tingle, he couldn't help wishing it was for him.

"I'm sorry," she said when he didn't speak. "He's your father,

I shouldn't have—" She broke off, then ended flatly, "It's none of my business."

My God, Josh thought, it had been personal. That anger, that heat had been for him. It is your business, he wanted to tell her, and that stunned him more than anything else had.

"I'm sorry, Josh," she repeated when he didn't speak but only stared at her with an expression she couldn't fathom.

"It's all right," he said at last, his voice strangely vibrant with a note she'd never heard before. "I've just never had anybody want to...fight for me before."

She blushed, more at the odd tone that seemed to tickle her spine than at his words, but she held his gaze.

"It's just not fair," she said rather vehemently. "Children shouldn't have to deal with that kind of betrayal. It can cripple as much as a beating."

Josh shook his head in awe at her fervor. He supposed she was right; it had been a long, long time before he had finally become convinced that they had been wrong, that he wasn't what that angry old man had always told him he was. And it made sense that he had been driven by that need to show both of them that they'd been wrong about him. He even acknowledged that it did occasionally rise to haunt him that they would never concede an inch.

"The only way some people can build themselves up is to tear someone else down," she said softly.

"I know. It took me a long time to figure that out. To understand that it was them, not me." He shrugged. "I don't think they ever really wanted a kid. I came along late, and unexpectedly, I think. They were complete with just each other, and I don't think they ever forgave me for disrupting their lives."

Hunter glanced up at the building behind them, seeing more than just the structure itself, seeing all it stood for, all it had taken to build it.

"I've found," she said slowly, "that parents like yours are sometimes afraid of their own children. They see them as...competition, I suppose. They're afraid of their talent, their ability, as if by surpassing them the child takes something away from them. So they try to crush the child before that happens."

She was right, he thought, although he'd never thought of it quite that way. But he had put that behind him, and what was filling him with emotion now was not the lingering shadow of his father's injustice but the fierceness of Hunter's reaction. He found himself at a loss for words in the face of it, and could only shake his head once again.

"But it didn't crush you, did it?" Her voice was soft, almost tender, and he swallowed heavily. "It's his loss, really. He has an incredible son, and he'll never know it."

"God, Hunter!"

The words burst from him; she was tearing him apart with that soft voice, with the look in her eyes when she spoke those words that were balm on an old, half-forgotten wound. He reached for her, the restraint that had stopped him earlier vanishing in the fervency of what he was feeling.

Hunter didn't remember her own warnings to herself in time. By the time she did, she was in his arms, and all her resistance seemed to drain away. His arms were tight around her, and his warmth comforting against the dawn chill.

She didn't know exactly when or how it changed, only that one minute she was comfortably relaxed, thinking of how good it felt to let go, just for a moment, of the strain of those past days, and in the next minute tensely aware. Aware of the strength of his arms around her, of the solid length of his body pressed against her. And above all of how good it felt to be held by him. She should have known, she thought numbly. She should have known by now what happened to her when he touched her.

She felt him turn his head slightly, tilting it so his cheek was resting gently against her hair. She felt his breath warm and soft against her ear, and her nerves began to tingle. In spite of herself a little shiver went through her. She told herself to move, to pull away; instead, she found herself turning her own head until her cheek was pressed against his chest.

She heard the beat of his heart beneath her ear and heard it speed up even as she listened to its steady strength. The rough-textured cotton shirt he wore did nothing to shield her from his heat, and she felt an answering warmth begin to rise within her.

He shifted again, and she felt the soft press of his lips against her hair. A shiver rippled through her, and his arms tightened around her in response. Stop it, she told herself, ordering her recalcitrant body to obey her mind's demand to retreat.

Josh felt her movement, felt the tension building in her. "Hunter?" he said softly, his voice deep and husky.

She twisted in his arms, tilted her head to look at him, to tell him this had to stop, that they couldn't begin this again, that she had to leave. She had all the reasons why on the tip of her tongue, but when she looked up into piercing blue eyes, they vanished. Those eyes were enthralling, and right now warm with a look that matched the sound of his voice.

"Josh..."

She'd meant to sound firm, unshaken; instead, the whispered name came out as an entreaty. What was he doing to her? She had to fight this; it was wrong, it was only a reaction. They'd been under such strain for so long, it was only natural. That had to be the explanation, for the kisses, for her fevered response.

How could she not have realized? How many times had she seen it? They hate you, fight you every step of the way until they come to depend on you, so much that they decided that they'd really loved you all along....

Then his mouth was on hers, and the reasons, the common sense, didn't matter anymore. All her logical rationale vanished, crowded out by the new, burgeoning sensations that were rippling through her. She shivered, wondering how she could when she was warmer than she could ever remember being. His lips were soft yet demanding as they separated hers, his tongue hot and exciting as it probed gently yet insistently into the depths of her mouth.

Hunter was barely aware of slipping her hands up to lock behind his head; she only knew she wanted more. She heard him make a low sound, then felt his hands slide down her back to her waist. Her fingers tangled into the thick hair at his nape as this time it was she who deepened the kiss; it was her tongue probing and plunging, meeting his in a sensual dance that fired her blood.

The small sign, that indication of desire returned, singed Josh to the core. He hadn't expected it, not after that look in her eyes in the restaurant. He'd labeled himself a fool for thinking she might want him back, but it hadn't stopped him. He'd only known how very good she felt in his arms, and had at last surrendered to the seemingly unbearable urge; he just had to kiss her again. That she had not fought him, had not, as Sam had said she was capable of doing, torn him apart, had startled him.

With agonizing slowness he slid one hand up her slender rib cage as he trailed soft kisses down the side of her throat. She let her head loll back, as if to give him more of that delicate column, and his pulse began to hammer in his ears.

"Hunter?"

His voice sounded raw, strained, but he was beyond caring. When she looked up at him from beneath half-lowered lashes, when she reached up to gently run a slender finger along the line of his jaw, when she softly whispered, "Yes," he was beyond talking at all.

He'd never felt this before, this exultation in every sign of desire returned; he supposed he'd never really cared much before. Or perhaps he'd just never believed it before, after Cynthia had destroyed any faith he might have had in a woman's honest response. But he never doubted Hunter's; if he had come to learn anything in the past week, it was that she was honest to the bone. Something he hadn't believed possible in a woman, until Hunter.

His hand crept upward over the rich green silk of her blouse, irresistibly drawn to the beckoning curve of her breast. He felt her tense slightly as his fingertips reached the soft fullness, and he stopped when he remembered that she had seemed frightened before. But the memory of that warm flesh rounding into his hand made him groan, and he had to feel that tender flesh nestled in his palm again. He moved slowly, cupping that flesh tenderly, as if it were some precious, fragile treasure he'd discovered.

Hunter gasped with surprised pleasure when his thumb slid up to caress the tingling peak of her breast, pleasure at the instant response of that rapidly puckering flesh and surprise at the strength of the echoing warmth that began in some buried core deep within her. Never had she felt so much so fast; the speed of it was leaving her breathless.

Josh groaned again, wrenching his hand away with tortured regret. He knew he had to slow down; he had to remember where they were, but he wanted to know, to caress every inch of her silken skin, every curve and hollow. He wanted to kiss her until she was hot and needing as he was. He wanted—

Stop it, he hissed to himself. In about another second you're going to be out of control. It's been too damn long. Sure, Kincaid. You've been living like a monk for months now, that's all it is. It's just been so long that a few kisses send you over the edge. Keep telling yourself that.

It wasn't working. And right now he didn't care. All he cared about was the slender, vital woman in his arms, the woman whose slightest touch sent fire racing along his nerves, the woman who could turn him into a shaking, uncertain kid again at the mere thought that she might want him as he did her. And God, he did want her.

He pressed her to him until Hunter thought the sheer fire of him would sear her flesh. Her breasts were crushed against his chest, and she could feel the new sensitivity of her nipples as they rose to his heat.

It was like being drawn into a wall of solid flame, and she felt her strength melt away in the face of its heat; she wondered if she would ever be able to move away. She felt his hands on the gentle curve of her hips, urging; she didn't resist. Couldn't resist.

Then a shock wave rippled through her as he pulled her tightly against his hips. He growled low in his throat, a sound barely recognizable as her name, but what suddenly tensed her every muscle was the feel of him, hot and hard and demanding, pressing against her hip.

Every warning bell, every alarm her mind possessed went off at the feel of that rigidly aroused flesh. With a strength born of desperation, she twisted away from him.

He wore a dazed expression as he looked at her, his eyes still hot, his lips parted as he drew in a ragged breath. He swallowed heavily, then lowered his eyes as he sagged back against the cab of the truck.

"Josh." It came out as a hoarse little whisper, and she had to try again. "Josh, I'm sorry. I should have known better—I did know better—than to let it go so far. This was a mistake."

"So I gathered." His voice was thick, still husky with the lingering echoes of passion.

Hunter gathered the shreds of her composure. "I know what you're feeling—I've seen it before. And I understand."

"You understand what?" He looked up then, a hint of the old ice beginning to show once more in his face and in his voice.

"It's only natural," she said, her effort to sound reassuring only resulting in a soft tremor in her tone. "People often feel...an attachment to someone they share a horrible experience with. Bonds are formed under stress. But that's all it is, and you mustn't mistake it for something else."

"Is that what you think?"

His voice grated on nerves already strained, and his eyes were as icy as they had been that first day. Hunter couldn't answer; the switch from gentle, caressing lover to angry iceberg was too abrupt, too complete. It was as if that other Josh had never existed.

"All right," he said harshly, as if she had spoken, "then we'll forget it ever happened. Any of it."

He climbed into the truck and slammed the door with a force that made her take a quick step back. Without another look he started the engine and roared away.

Forget it ever happened? Not likely, Hunter thought with aching ruefulness. What had just happened to her today was unlike anything she'd ever felt in her life, and she wasn't apt to forget it. Ever. She sighed and somewhat shakily walked back to her car.

Chapter 9

Hunter crossed item number one off her list as she walked slowly down the Barrington's long driveway toward her car. She had found nothing new at the pool house, except for the piece of news provided by Sam that Rob's parents were on their way home from New York.

"It was incredible," the detective said. "They were just as upset over having to cut their trip short as finding out what Rob did. Their second question, after asking where he was, was if there'd been any publicity about it."

"Somehow I'm not surprised," Hunter returned with disdain.

"Speaking of which," Sam said, "the juvenile court officer wants to talk to you. Wants your assessment of the kid, I think."

She nodded. "I'll call today. You ready to get started?"

"I guess. I still think you should handle the team, though. You've developed such a rapport, after all."

He was teasing, and she wrinkled her nose at him. "Get moving, Sammy. I've got some door-to-door to do."

"All right, I'm going. Have a— Oops, looks like you've got company." She looked up, then around, not seeing anyone. "Your car," Sam said.

Her heart gave a little leap when she saw the tall, lean figure leaning against the front fender of her car. She didn't think she made a sound, but Sam was looking at her curiously.

"You all right?"

She couldn't seem to speak, so she nodded.

"You sure? You look awfully pale." He looked over at Josh, close enough now to see that his expression was as dark as hers was pale. "Uh, you want me to talk to him?"

Yes, her heart screamed, I can't deal with this. Then her mind, cold with scorn, rose to batter down that heartfelt plea. You may be a lot of things, Garrett, but you're not a runner.

"No. I'll do it. Go ahead and get started."

Sam looked at her doubtfully, but when she gave a short jerk of her head, he took the cue and left. Hunter crossed the last few yards to her car at a determinedly steady pace.

If only he didn't look so damn good, she thought ruefully. He had showered, shaved the beard that had shadowed his jaw and changed, she saw, into a pair of faded black jeans—which did criminal things to his legs and hips—and a teal blue cotton sweater that made his eyes fairly leap out at her. His hair was still damp, curling against the back of his neck, but she knew it would dry straight and thick. And she knew what she would smell when she got close enough: that woodsy-scented after-shave he wore. She knew so much about this man. And so little.

She came to a stop at the front bumper of the car, a safe three feet away. He didn't move, just lounged against the fender, his long legs extended and crossed at the ankle, looking at her impassively.

"I didn't expect to see you here." She had tried to sound calm, but wound up sounding cool instead. It didn't seem to matter; his expression didn't change.

"You said you were going to start here." His voice was, if anything, cooler than hers.

"Yes, I am. What do you want?"

He stood up then. "I'm going with you."

She sighed inwardly. "No."

"Yes. I'm through with sitting around, waiting. This, as you said, is a different ball game."

"Yes, it is. But that doesn't mean I can have a civilian tagging along on an official investigation."

She expected that familiar temper to flare, but he only shrugged. "I can go with you or 'tag along,' but I'm going to be there. I'm not sitting at home on my hands while Jason is in trouble."

"That's exactly where you should be. If a call comes—"

"The recorder is on, and Mrs. Elliott is there. Along with one of your colleagues from Aliso Beach, who arrived this morning, as you well know."

She did; she'd put in the order for an officer to stand by at the house and monitor the wiretap on the line.

"Look," she tried again, "you can't just move in on a police investigation. There are other questions, the city would be liable if you got hurt—"

"I won't." Something flickered briefly in the cool gaze. "After all, I'll be with a black belt in karate."

Hunter bit back her surprised exclamation. Damn you, Sam, you talk too much. When the hell did you bring that up? And why?

"Josh, you can't." Even now, she couldn't quite slip back into that formal "Mr. Kincaid."

"I can. I am. Do I go with you, or just follow you around?"

She glanced at the pickup that was parked behind her car. He probably would, she thought. No, he definitely would. Why was he so damn calm? Where was the temper she'd born the brunt of for days now?

"Would it do me any good to bring up the fact that interfering with an officer is against the law?" she asked dryly.

"No," he said easily. "I won't be interfering. I won't even talk, if that's what you want. But I *will* be there."

Hunter let out an explosive breath and slammed her notepad down on the hood of the car.

"Are we through wasting time?" he asked politely.

"Damn," she muttered, then recovered herself. "Just remind me to get a waiver for you to sign," she said sweetly, "so the city doesn't have to pay your hospital bills."

"Certainly," he said blandly, and walked around to the passenger door.

The rest of the day was exhausting, and from Josh's point of view, fruitless. From door to door they went, from unhelpful face to unhelpful face. Hunter kept copious notes, including everything from houses where no one was home, to be revisited later, to descriptions of any vehicle anyone had seen in the past week. She took the license numbers of every car on the street and wrote down the times when everyone who wasn't at home would be home to be talked to.

Josh began to see the drudgery behind the glamour most people thought of when they thought of a cop's life. And his already considerable respect for her grew, especially when he realized that she had been through this before, the first time. He knew she had to be as tired as he was, yet she kept on ceaselessly, stopping only to grab a can of soda from a convenience store at noon.

"You ever stop? Lunch, maybe?" he'd asked, only to be treated to a cool glance.

"You stowed away on this train—don't blame me if it isn't run the way you like it."

She had, he had to admit, a point. "Can you stow away on a train?" he'd asked mildly.

She'd looked at him oddly, as if he had suddenly become a puzzle she couldn't figure out. And his reaction when she mentioned that the Barringtons were reluctantly returning from New York to deal with their errant son did more than puzzle her; it amazed her.

"Where's Rob now?"

"With the child welfare people, until his parents get home."

"What happens then?"

"There'll be a hearing, at least, in front of a court-appointed hearing officer. As for any further action—" she shot him a sideways look "—that sort of depends on you."

"Me?"

"You're the victim of his extortion attempt."

He let out a short breath, then shook his head. "I'd say Rob's more of a victim than I am."

Her voice was carefully even. "You mean you don't want to pursue criminal charges?"

He shook his head again, sharper this time. When he didn't speak she asked softly, "Josh?"

"He's got enough problems," he said suddenly, roughly. "I know about prize parents, remember? Besides, I think you were right. I think he thought he was...helping Jason."

Hunter had been trying to figure out what had happened, what had brought about the tremendous change in Josh. When she would have expected him to go over the edge, he had instead made an incredible turnabout. He had found some inner strength that astounded her with its quiet steadiness. And now he was astonishing her even more with his quiet, generous understanding of the boy who had struck out at him so blindly.

"You're...really something, Josh Kincaid."

His gaze flew to her face, searching. Neither of them had mentioned the episode in the Kincaid Industries parking lot. Josh seemed, to all appearances, to have done exactly what he'd said—forgotten it ever happened. That task was beyond her; it smoldered in her mind like an ember that refused to die. But now she wondered if he'd buried it quite as thoroughly as it seemed.

The memory of those fevered moments was still there later, when she sat at her commandeered desk making the first of the innumerable phone calls to people who hadn't been home this morning or afternoon. She had dropped him off back at his truck after a long, wearying afternoon that had produced little in the way of leads. No one seemed to have seen anything out of the ordinary, but she had expected nothing else in this community of walled estates.

She had to admit he had kept to his word. He hadn't interfered, had rarely even spoken. Yet his presence had somehow been comforting, in an odd sort of way she didn't stop to analyze; they had too much ground to cover.

His presence had also been disturbing. He was quietly polite, as if there had never been anything between them except a formal coolness. She had caught herself more than once sneaking a glance at him, noticing the way his hair gleamed darkly in the sun, the way the sleeves of his sweater were pushed up on tanned, muscular arms and the sinful way those black jeans cupped his buttocks. And no matter how many times she delivered her silent lecture to herself, she hadn't been able to stop herself from looking.

She paused before making the next call, rubbing at eyes that were screaming for sleep. She knew she would have to rest some time; thirty-six hours without sleep was beginning to show. She'd make ten more calls, she thought, then she'd spare herself an hour or so on the couch that had been her bed for longer than she cared to remember.

As she reached for the phone, it rang, and it took a moment for her fatigued brain to make the switch from calling to answering. She smothered a yawn as she picked it up.

"Investigator Garrett."

"It's Josh."

She sat up straight; something in his voice snapped her awake. "What's wrong?" she asked abruptly, forgoing the niceties.

"An envelope. A big one, with something more than a letter in it. Plain. It's not from my office."

He broke off, and she thought she heard him take in a deep breath.

"At the house?"

"Yes. Mrs. Elliott found it on the porch."

"I'll be right there. Is Officer Jordan there?"

"Yes. He said not to touch it anymore "

"Good. Tell him I'll call CSI."

She hit the stairs at a run, adrenaline pounding through her system, erasing her exhaustion. She stopped by the downstairs office of the crime scene investigator, thankfully finding him there. It was the same officer who had been to the Barrington house last night, so her explanation was brief.

She was at the house in minutes, the lights on in the rarely used living room telling her where everyone was. Officer Jordan had apparently been watching for her, because he was out the door before she stopped the car.

"What have we got?" she asked after greeting him.

"Manila envelope. Something stuffed in it. Don't know how long it had been there—Mrs. Elliott used the side door, and Mr. Kincaid came in through the garage."

So the pickup got the garage these days, she thought, having noticed the luxury sedan sitting rather forlornly in the driveway.

"You've checked the area?"

"Yeah. No footprints, no sign of which way he came from. Mrs. Elliott called the neighbors. One of them heard a car at about six, but didn't see anything. She thought it was Mr. Kincaid, but he wasn't home yet."

"I know." She looked over her shoulder at the sound of another car, and saw the CSI officer pulling in. "Show him where it was, will you, Mark? I'll be inside if he needs me."

She saw Josh the moment she came in, sitting in one of the wingback chairs, staring at the envelope on the cold marble table in front of him. He looked up as she came into the room, his face still impassive. She crossed the room and knelt beside the table.

It was about eleven by fourteen inches, a standard manila envelope that could be purchased anywhere, and whatever it contained was uneven and wadded up. Its blankness was marred only by a gray mark on one corner. She leaned forward to inspect the discoloration.

"Mrs. Elliott stepped on it before she realized it was there."

His words were even, controlled. Hunter's eyes lifted to his. They were cool, yet that fire she had caught glimpses of earlier was there, as well, stronger now, as if he had focused and begun to stoke it. She nodded at what he'd said, then went to the door to call in the CSI officer.

Mrs. Elliott, clearly distressed, brought her a cup of coffee. After asking her a few brief questions about the envelope, Hunter gently told the older woman to go on up to bed, thanking her for the coffee. I hope it's black, strong, and ninety percent caffeine, she thought.

The results on the envelope were as much—or as little—as she'd expected. No prints, and traces of fabric marks on the metal clasp, indicating that whoever left it had been wearing gloves. Still, she was careful when she opened it. She undid the clasp, lifted the flap and peered inside, aware of Josh's eyes on her every second.

When she saw what it was, her eyes flicked to Josh, then back to the envelope as she hesitated.

"Go ahead." His voice was harsh, but steady.

Clasping it with two careful fingers, she drew out the envelope's contents.

She heard Josh's intake of breath and knew without asking that the baseball cap she held was Jason's. It was the same team cap she had seen Rob Barrington wear, as well as the rest of the players.

"Are you sure?" she asked, knowing she didn't have to explain her question.

"Yes. That stain is where he dropped it in the mud once."

Josh didn't add that the boy had been so miserable about ruining his new hat that he had moped for days, until in irritation Josh had threatened to throw it away altogether. He had learned at last that regrets didn't solve anything. Thanks to Hunter. So many things he hadn't known until Hunter.

She set the cap down on the table, then reached into the envelope once more. Again, it was a sheet of lined notebook paper that could be purchased anywhere, impossible to trace. And the words on it were carefully printed in block letters, with plain, blue ballpoint ink, both with virtually no unique characteristics. Clearly they were dealing with a much more serious threat than young Rob Barrington's halfhearted extortion attempt.

The words were clear, to the point and specific.

> We have Jason. It will cost you a million to get him back. You'll be called on Saturday with further instructions. Be at the phone booth at the Aliso Business Park at 6 AM. I see a cop, you'll never see the kid alive again.

She was aware of Josh's eyes fastened on her. She opened her mouth to speak, then stopped. There was nothing she could say to soften this blow. She reached out to hand the note to him. He moved to take it, then hesitated, looking at her.

"It's all right. He's been much too careful to have slipped up and handled this without his gloves. But hold it by the edges anyway—we might get lucky."

She watched his face as he read the demand. His expression never faltered, but that heat glowing in the blue eyes went up another notch in intensity. He handed the note back to her, and she gave it carefully to the CSI man, along with the cap. He gathered them up and his equipment.

"I'll leave 'em in the evidence locker at the station," he said, and when Hunter nodded, left. At a nod from her, Officer Jordan followed him.

Josh got to his feet and crossed to the big picture-window that looked down the long driveway. He stood there silently looking out for a long moment. When at last he spoke, there was a hint of that heat in the tautness of his voice.

"It's for real, isn't it?"

"Yes. There's not a doubt in my mind that this one's for real."

"It seems the ante's gone up."

"Yes."

"Is that enough?"

She knew what he meant. "A million is still low, relatively speaking. And there are...other things that bother me."

"Like?"

"The wait. It's stupid to give us so much time to set up on the call location. He's either got Jason so far away already it doesn't matter that we could trace the call, or we're dealing with another amateur."

Josh winced but asked steadily enough, "Which do you think?"

She looked thoughtful. "Low ransom, too much time..."

"Amateur?" He guessed which way she was leaning. "But then what about the wait?"

"Maybe he just wants you to sweat a little."

Josh gave a harsh, mirthless chuckle. "What does he think I've been doing?"

"But not for him." Josh's brow shot up. "A lot of kidnappers get a thrill out of the feeling of power, even if that's not what they went into it for."

"You keep saying he. The note says *we*."

"But he slipped and said 'if *I*' see a cop. He probably said 'we' so you don't think he's working alone."

"But you think he is?"

"Just a hunch."

"I know about your hunches."

Hunter looked at him, startled. She had been on edge ever since she'd got here, waiting for him to blow up or strike out in his frustration. It didn't happen. Dan had been breaking things at this point; Josh just sat there composedly. With that fire gleaming in his eyes.

"What about the place?" he asked. "I don't think I know it."

"It's out in an industrial area, next to the railroad tracks. It's not in Aliso Beach, really—it's county area on the border of the city. And it's also usually deserted on weekends. Maybe that's why the wait until Saturday."

"A phone booth." His mouth twisted wryly. "A little trite, isn't it?"

"Maybe. But for the first contact, not unusual."

"'Further instructions,'" Josh muttered. "I wonder how long he's going to play this game."

"We won't know until Saturday. In the meantime we'll try to be as low-profile as possible. He might be watching the house."

"We checked every damn street between here and Barrington's this afternoon," he said dryly.

"I know. But we still could have missed something. And I haven't had a chance to check out all those license numbers we got yet."

"So now what? Never mind," he said quickly. "I know. We wait."

"You wait. I get back to work."

He glanced at his watch. "You plan on sleeping sometime this week?"

"I could ask you the same thing."

"I'm going jogging."

She stared at him blankly. "What?"

"Jogging. You know, running shoes, sweat, gasping for breath?"

"What I know is, you are nuts. You need sleep, not marathon practice."

"So do you, but I don't see you slowing down. Besides, who knows what I might run across out there."

Realization dawned, and she got quickly to her feet. "Oh, no you don't! You're not going out there snooping around—"

"You're right. I'm going jogging."

"Josh," she said warningly.

"Am I under house arrest or something?"

"Of course not, but—"

"Then I'm going jogging," he repeated calmly.

Hunter crossed to the big window where he stood. She wanted to see his face to see if there was a clue.... Once again she tried to analyze the change in him, tried to define the new light in his eyes.

"What is it, Josh?" she said finally, softly. "What happened to you?"

Something about the silky softness in her voice and the way she was studying him with those huge green eyes made him go suddenly warm. And made it impossible for him not to answer her. He knew the answer, although he hadn't realized it until she asked him. He should have known she would sense it, he thought. She had probably known something had changed before you did.

"I can fight this," he said quietly.

"This?"

"Jason wanted to come home," he said, and the sudden ice in his voice was as implacable as the eyes she remembered from that first day in the office. "He wanted to come home, and somebody stopped him."

Hunter understood then. Josh had an enemy now. Maybe not a face or a name, but an enemy just the same, a tangible one that could be fought, could be brought down. And just as he had years ago, when the enemy had been his father, and later, when it had been Cynthia, and still later, when it had been those who had insisted a man with his scruples couldn't succeed, he would beat them. As he'd said, he could fight this.

"If he hurts my son—"

"He won't. Jason is his meal ticket."

"That hasn't stopped a lot of others from—"

"Take it easy, Josh," Hunter interjected quickly, not liking the barely contained anger that flared suddenly in his eyes.

"I'm fine."

'Just don't get any ideas about becoming a vigilante here. You could endanger Jason."

"I'm fine," he repeated. She looked at him warily. He turned his head to look out the window into the darkened yard. When he looked back at her, the anger had faded, to be replaced by a softness she hadn't thought ever to see again.

"Don't worry. I really am all right, now."

"You're sure?"

He nodded. "I just...it's been a long time since I've had to fight. Things had been going my way for too long, I guess. I thought for a while I'd forgotten how."

"I doubt that."

He gave her a smile that startled her with its warmth. "I hadn't forgotten, really. I was just rusty."

"I'd say," Hunter said assessingly, studying that new light in his eyes, "that any rust you built up is disappearing fast."

That smile again. "Before, all I could think about was what I'd done wrong, how I'd driven Jason away." He shook his head. "But he still wanted to come home. I finally figured out that that was the most important thing."

Hunter shook her head in wonder. She had hoped he would reach that realization, but she'd never guessed at what an effect it would have on him if he did. "I'm glad," she said softly, a smile curving her lips.

Josh swallowed tightly at the warmth in her voice, at the glow in her eyes. He hadn't meant to let down his guard with her, not again, but he couldn't seem to stop.

"I couldn't fight it before," he said with a grimace, "because I knew it was my fault. In my own way, I was as bad as my father, and I hated myself for it."

"It's hard to defend yourself when you're not sure you're worth it."

Even this she understood, he thought in amazement. Then he caught the flicker in the depths of the green eyes, and realization struck. Of course she understood.

"Timmy wasn't your fault at all," he said softly.

Her head shot up, and her eyes widened as she stared at him. How had he guessed? How had he known how she had battled against that creeping guilt, wondering if perhaps Dan had been right, that somehow it had all been her fault? And most incredibly, why, in the midst of this horrible new development in Jason's disappearance, and after what she'd said to him this morning—God, was it only this morning?—did he even bother to extend this gentle support?

"I...thank you." She turned her eyes to the window, wondering if she should say what she'd been thinking about since this morning when he had told her about his parents. He needed to hear it, she decided at last. He might not believe it, but at least it would give him something to think about besides guilt.

"You know," she began slowly, "it's not really all your fault about Jason, either."

Turning his back to the window, he stared at her for a second, then he let out a swift breath before his mouth hardened into that implacable line she knew so well. That set, forbidding line that made it nearly impossible to believe that that mouth could do such hot, exciting things to her.

"It's my fault," he said flatly.

"But if—"

"It's my fault," he repeated. "I won't try and run away from it."

No, she thought, you wouldn't. Running away isn't in your vocabulary. "I didn't say none of it was your fault."

He looked blank. "It either is or it isn't."

"Is it? Is it really that cut-and-dried?"

He was beginning to get irritated at this conversation that made no sense to him. He opened his mouth to say so, then shut it without speaking. Hunter rarely, he had learned, said things that made no sense, only things that didn't make sense at the time. "What," he said carefully, "are you getting at?"

"That it's not all your fault if that's all you knew."

"All I—" He broke off, took a long breath and tried again. "What is that supposed to mean?"

"All you knew about how parents treat their kids is what you learned from your father. You knew what was wrong, but that didn't tell you what's right."

He stared at her.

"Don't you see? Just knowing what's wrong isn't enough, not if you don't have a clue about what's right." She took a breath. "When was the last time your father hugged you?"

His shocked expression gave her the answer she'd expected: never.

"It's the little things like that, Josh, not just the verbal abuse. You can't learn to be a warm parent from a cold one. You had to teach yourself." She wanted to reach out to take him, to take his hand, but she didn't dare. "And you did. You wanted Jason enough to bargain with a woman like Cynthia for him. And you never stopped loving him, even when it hurt you just to look at him. That's more than your father ever did. All you have to do is learn how to show it to Jason."

She took in a deep breath. "You love him enough to learn. And that's why you could never be like your father."

She saw him take it in, could almost see him analyzing it, assessing it. She wondered if he'd find anything in her words that he thought was worth keeping. After the way they'd parted this morning, and the chilly atmosphere of the rest of the day, she wouldn't have bet any money on it. So she was startled, even stunned when he spoke, his voice rich and low and tender.

"You're determined to save me from myself, aren't you?"

She colored. "I just think you have enough to carry without taking on a lot of misguided guilt on top of it."

She saw the barest shake of his head, a movement that was almost imperceptible. Then his arms moved, lifted from his sides towards her. The movement stopped, and she saw both of his hands curl into fists. Abruptly he turned back to the window.

Hunter didn't know which shocked her more, the fact that he had, even after this morning, still wanted to reach for her, or that she was fiercely disappointed that he had stopped. The warm, vivid memory of how she had felt in his arms, of how his mouth had sent that rippling, searing heat through her rose up to flood her with an echoing warmth.

She had to stop this. She couldn't go on like this, letting her emotions and her imagination run away with her. She had to stop letting his slightest touch send her blood pressure soaring and her heart racing.

Right, Garrett, she said to herself dryly. And just how do you intend to stop it when just looking at him turns your bones to water? As if to prove her own words, her eyes went to him seemingly of their own volition.

His face was in shadow as he stared out the window, one forearm braced over his head against the frame as he leaned against it. The room light behind him threw his profile into stark relief, seeming to stress the lean lines of his body. As she found her assessment of her reaction to him to be all too accurate.

As she watched, he lowered his head to rest it on the window frame below his arm. His lashes lowered, and for a moment he looked worn, beaten and utterly weary. Hunter's heart twisted inside her, and she felt the stinging of tears behind her eyelids.

"Josh?"

She saw him stiffen, then straighten, as if in denial of a moment of weakness.

"Will you please rest?"

He didn't look at her. "Will you?"

She sighed. "I'll grab a couple of hours when I get back to the office."

"Stay here."

She stared at him, smothering a gasp at the images those two simple words brought to her mind. Knock it off, Garrett. He didn't mean it like that. He turned his head to look at her, and for the briefest moment she thought he had. Then that look that had seemed strangely like hunger faded.

"Mrs. Elliott can get a room ready. At least you'll have a bed instead of a couch."

"Josh—"

"And I'll postpone jogging until morning."

The implication was clear; if she didn't stay, not only would he not rest, but he would also persist in going out into the night on the off chance that he might find something.

"Not only have you remembered how to fight, Kincaid," she said sourly, "you've remembered how to fight dirty. Emotional blackmail is not fair."

He merely shrugged, but she thought she saw the faintest of twitches at the corner of his mouth. "If you hurry, you'll make it to sleep by midnight." As if she had agreed, he turned and walked into the kitchen to speak to Mrs. Elliott.

Hunter wasn't quite sure why she gave in. In fact, didn't realize she had until Mrs. Elliott called down the stairs that her room was ready and that there were clean towels in the bathroom. She was cornered then; she wouldn't offend the kindly woman for the world. She ruefully congratulated Josh on his adept maneuvering once more as they made their way upstairs.

"I can see now why things tend to go your way," she said dryly.

"Nice to know I haven't lost the knack."

He paused beside her at the door of the room Mrs. Elliott had prepared. There was a long, awkward moment when neither of them spoke, and sudden tension crackled between them. Their eyes met, the knowledge of what would happen if they dared to close that last small space between them here, now, leaping between them. Then Josh moved abruptly, taking a half step back.

"Good night," he said gruffly.

"Yes," Hunter said, trying to control the sudden quickening of her breathing.

She saw his hands curl into fists again, the tendons in his wrists standing out with the strain. He sucked in a breath and turned away. On legs that were none too steady, she took a step toward the room.

"Hunter?"

At the slightly ragged sound of his voice, she looked back over her shoulder.

"Do me a favor," he said unsteadily.

"What?"

"Lock the door."

Chapter 10

Hunter awoke early with no real recollection of having fallen asleep. She did remember, however, lying awake long after her weary body had at last relaxed. Her mind had refused to slow down, and knowing that Josh was just down the hall hadn't helped. Still, she supposed she felt better than she had.

How, she said to herself as she made her way groggily to the bathroom, had she got herself into this mess? It was the question she had been asking in the dark last night; the answer was no clearer in the light of dawn.

How had he done it? How had he got past the barriers she had so carefully built up in the past six years? Not only got past them, but made her feel things she'd never felt before? Dream things she'd never dreamed before, long for things she'd never longed for before?

She hoped the blast of the shower would clear things up. Mrs. Elliott had made certain she had everything she needed: shampoo, comb, brush, even a hair dryer. She wondered if they were just extras, or if they had once belonged to the ruthless phantom whose presence seemed to linger in this huge house.

Josh had really had his share of prize people in his life, she thought as she lathered her hair. It was amazing he hadn't turned out twisted himself, let alone that he had done what he'd done.

And just like that her thoughts were back in that same groove. You're a basket case, she told herself as she dried off with the thick, sweet-smelling towel and reached for the small makeup bag that was in her purse.

She'd meant to leave quietly, hoping to slip out without awakening anyone. She only went into the kitchen because she recalled seeing a notepad there, and she wanted to leave a thank-you for Mrs. Elliott. If she was consciously avoiding mentioning Josh, even to herself, she didn't admit it. And the moment she stepped inside the cheerful room, she knew it was pointless anyway.

Barefoot, he was sitting at the table in the breakfast nook, staring down at a steaming cup. His hair was still tousled, as if he'd only run his fingers through it upon arising. But for once she barely noticed it; her eyes seemed to be immovably fastened elsewhere. He had on the snug, faded black jeans from yesterday, and the clean shirt he'd slipped on was unbuttoned and hung open.

She couldn't seem to take her eyes off that wide band of bare flesh. She could see the sprinkling of dark hair over his breastbone between twin swells of muscle, could see where it gave way to smooth, tanned skin over the ridged flatness of his abdomen, then on down to that intriguing path of hair that began at his navel and arrowed downward to disappear into the low-slung waistband of his jeans.

As if he'd sensed her scrutiny, he looked up. And just in time, Hunter thought, struggling to beat down the flush that was rising to her cheeks. She had been staring at his chest, wondering just how far she would have to slide her hands beneath the open edges of that shirt before she found the flat, male nipples. And that was only after forcing herself to look away from that tempting trail of hair that led—

"You're up early."

His voice cut across her immodest thoughts, and she tried to regain her scattered poise.

"So are you. Or did you even sleep?"

"For a while."

Was there an edge to his voice or not? She wasn't sure.

"But not enough," she said, looking at his still red-rimmed eyes.

"I'll get by." He lifted his cup. "Coffee's over there."

Oh, no, she thought. I'm not sitting here across the table from him for morning coffee in the picture of domesticity. I'm in enough trouble already, without adding that to my list of mental images.

"No, thanks," she said hastily. "I have to get going. Tell Mrs. Elliott thank-you for me, will you?"

He nodded as he set down his cup and stood up. "You're going to the station?"

She nodded. "I want to get started running down those license numbers."

"Then?"

She shrugged. "Back to the foot beat. It's all we have right now."

"Is there anyone left to talk to?"

"A few. And there are a couple of other people I want to track down. Gardeners, pool men, that kind of thing."

He seemed to hesitate before he spoke again. "I have to go to the office for a while, before the place falls apart," he began, "but..."

Hunter sighed. "Why do I get the feeling I'm going to have company again whether I like it or not?"

"Because you're very perceptive."

Hunter didn't know whether to laugh or groan in frustration. "Josh—"

"When do you plan to start?"

Hunter rolled her eyes, but knew she was going to give in. She doubted that anything would happen; she expected the same kind of fruitless day they'd had yesterday. It would be safe enough.

"I'll pick you up," she said wryly.

He looked surprised, then doubtful.

"I mean it."

He was still suspicious. "You gave in awfully easily."

"For a reason." She'd been thinking about this, too. "Because there may be a time when the answer is no. I'll go as far as I can with this, Josh, but when I do say no, I'll mean it. No appeal. Understood?"

His look of skepticism faded, to be replaced by a barely suppressed smile. "Does that mean no more fighting?"

"Somehow I doubt it." She felt her own mouth twitch in spite of herself. "Especially since I reserve the right to argue."

"I'd expect nothing less of you, Investigator Garrett," he returned formally. Both their smiles broke free for a fleeting moment before the grim reality rushed back.

It was as she went into the living room to pick up her jacket that she had the first sense of something wrong. It was no more than a tiny tickle at the back of her neck, but she had long ago learned to trust these little feelings she got. She strolled over to the window as she slipped on the jacket, to all appearances casually glancing out as she straightened the collar. And then she froze.

It was only for the briefest of moments, and she covered it with a shrug of her shoulders as if settling the jacket sleeves. She turned away as if she'd seen nothing and moved unhurriedly out of range of the window.

"Josh?"

He turned around to look at her from where he stood in the entryway, tugging on a pair of running shoes. For a second she smiled inwardly; Josh Kincaid could have bought the entire company that made those shoes ten times over, yet they were worn, almost ragged.

"Do you know anyone with a white van? Or a blue station wagon?"

His brow furrowed. "No. Not that I know of." He took a step toward her, but she threw up her hand to stop him. "What is it?" He asked sharply.

"I don't know." She knelt down, and to Josh's dismay, checked the small revolver in the holster at her ankle.

"Hunter—"

"I don't know," she bit out again, "but I'm going to find out."

"By yourself?"

"It may be nothing. There's just a little too much activity at the end of your driveway to suit me."

He tugged on the second shoe. "Okay, let's go find out."

"You're waiting here."

"Afraid not."

"Josh, it's my job."

"It's my driveway."

Hunter let out a compressed breath through clenched teeth. Josh crossed to the door and waited. Damn, she thought. He could be so stubborn! Thinking she'd better save her official "no" for something a bit more imperative, she gave up.

They were no more than two steps out the front door when all questions were answered. And in a way Hunter had both dreaded and not expected so soon.

Josh froze in his tracks the instant the door of the van slid back and two figures came tumbling out, both with hands full.

"What the—"

The first two were followed by three from the blue station wagon, equally laden down. Both Josh and Hunter had faced enough press conferences to recognize the equipment; cameras, tape recorders, steno pads. The only thing missing was the video cameras, and Hunter guessed that was only because they hadn't been certain Josh was here.

She didn't recognize any of them, and guessed they were mostly locals, free-lancers maybe; she knew most of the reporters on the state or national beat. They had considerably more class than this bunch.

"Mr. Kincaid! Can you tell us—?"

"Are there any new develop—?"

"Is it true your son is—?"

They had poured through the gate, heedlessly trampling the perfectly manicured flower beds. They were all jabbering at once, microphones thrusting forward, cameras snapping. Hunter felt Josh go rigid beside her, and one glance at his face told her an eruption was imminent. She took a quick step forward.

"Ladies and gentlemen, Mr. Kincaid has nothing to say at this time."

The portly man whose lank hair clung to the sides of his head looked her up and down.

"And who might you be?"

"The person who just told you all you're going to get this morning."

"Are you...an associate of Mr. Kincaid's?"

The question came from the sole woman in the group; it was directed at Hunter, but her eyes were pointedly fastened on Josh's bare chest beneath the shirt he'd neglected to button.

Hunter didn't miss the woman's insinuation, but neither did she respond to it. She'd had more experience than she cared to remember with the press, and she knew what could happen if you gave them what they were after—an agitated response. She had had the lesson pounded home the hard way in the days after Timmy's kidnapping, when the media's attention had been caught by the novelty of a police officer as a victim and had milked the story for all it was worth.

"I'm sorry, but there is no comment at this time," she said a little more sharply.

Ignoring her, the portly man turned on Josh. "Is it true your son is being held by terrorists to stop you from putting the Eureka II into production?"

Josh paled. "Get the hell out of here," he snapped.

Hunter put a restraining hand on his arm.

"Have you heard from them, Mr. Kincaid?" the woman reporter chimed in.

"That's—"

"—all, people." Hunter cut Josh off quickly. "Good day."

"And what exactly *is* your connection here, miss?" The portly man spoke again, with an unmistakable leer. Hunter would have written him off as a second-rate hack with a dirty mind had it not been for the clever gleam in his bright little eyes.

"Good *day*," she repeated, hanging on to her patience by a thread.

The man shifted his gaze back to Josh. "Do you always let your...ladies do your talking, Mr. Kincaid?"

"That's it," Josh barked. He took one step toward the shorter, much rounder man. "You've got ten seconds to get your mouth out of here."

"Why, Mr. Kincaid, how gallant! Protecting her honor?"

Josh cocked his arm back.

"Josh, no," Hunter grabbed his arm again. "That's just what they'd like."

After a moment he let his arm fall back. Hunter turned back to face the determined group.

"Gentlemen," she began, with emphasis on the drawled word, "and lady—" a bit more emphasis "—you are trespassing."

"We have a right to a story—"

"On public property. On private property, you have a right to nothing. Except," she said coldly, "an attorney if you persist."

The stout man eyed her with a dawning glimmer of curiosity. "You seem rather well versed, young lady. Are you perhaps an attorney yourself? A *personal* attorney?"

Hunter opened her mouth to reply, but before she could speak, Josh had stepped in. "I don't need an attorney to tell me that I'm within my rights to throw you out of here. Whether it's literally or figuratively is up to you."

Something in Hunter's stance and Josh's eyes seemed to convince them, and, muttering, they began to head back toward their vehicles.

"Damn," Josh swore softly as he watched them go. He didn't understand what had just happened. Not that they had been there; that had startled him, but he understood their interest. What he didn't understand was his own reaction. He'd been in front of countless groups of reporters, virtually every time Kincaid Industries began a new project. But never had he lost his cool like that. Of course, he'd never been ambushed in his own home before, he thought. That had to be the cause for his anger.

Right, Kincaid. You went high and to the right when they started in on Hunter. You might as well admit it. He glanced over at her as they walked back to where her car was parked.

She seemed calm enough on the surface, but he had learned her face well by now, and the slight tightness of her jaw didn't escape him.

"Hunter?" he said tentatively.

"Hmm."

"I'm sorry about...what they thought."

He smothered the little voice inside him that was saying that he was sorrier that what they had insinuated wasn't true. He didn't dare think of what it would be like to have faced that group after a night spent with Hunter in his arms. With Hunter in his bed. He stifled the groan that was trying to begin low in his throat.

"Don't feel sorry for me," she said. "Feel sorry for them. They have to make a living doing that."

"Why didn't you tell them who you were?"

"Because I didn't really want them to know. Until this is over, the fewer outsiders who know who I am, the better. If they think I'm...whatever they thought, instead of a cop, then they won't be printing that the police are treating this any differently than just a missing-persons case. And that's just what we want the kidnapper to think, for Jason's sake."

"You sound like you expected this."

"I did, eventually. You're a big name—it had to happen. I knew it when we went public with the flyers. I just didn't expect it so soon." She tossed her purse onto the front seat, then looked back at him. "They've found something they won't drop, Josh. If they think this is all connected to terrorism because of your project, it's even bigger news."

Josh let out a weary sigh, then his brow furrowed. "You mean headlines, don't you?"

"I'm afraid so."

"Great," he muttered.

"I know they can be a nuisance, but it is news."

She hated to defend the people who had so frequently made her life and work miserable, but they did have rights. They just didn't always remember where theirs ended and someone else's began.

He let out another tired breath as he shook his head. "It isn't that. I was just thinking about calling my parents." His mouth twisted wryly. "Oh well, it'll make their day. Proof that they were right all along."

He seemed to be joking, but Hunter sensed there was at least a grain of truth to his words. She hoped she never met those sorry excuses for parents. Then his attempt at sardonic humor vanished, and he looked at her seriously.

"You don't think there's a terrorist connection, do you."

It wasn't a question, but she hesitated. "I don't want to rule anything out. It's too early."

"You're hedging."

"Yes. But wisely. It really is too early to make any judgments like that. Remember, for all intents and purposes, Jason was just...taken less than thirty-six hours ago."

Pain flickered in Josh's eyes at the reminder dealt him by that single word, "taken." Then that anger that had been building, that had stirred up long-forgotten feelings, that had resurrected his dormant capacity to fight enormous odds and win, flared up again. He doggedly returned to the subject.

"I don't want a judgment, Hunter. I want your instinct."

"Josh—"

"It's been right every step of the way. Are you going to tell me that now that I trust it, you don't't?"

"There's a difference. I use it as a tool. You want it to hang your hope on."

"If you're right, it won't matter."

"And if I'm wrong?"

"Nothing will matter."

She saw then that he had realized all the possibilities suggested by the reporter's question. He knew that if the answer was yes, he would probably never see Jason again. He knew it, and it was poisoning him inside already, the thought that his work might be responsible for his son's peril.

She couldn't stand it. She'd looked upon hideous scenes of utter brutality, broken horrible news to too many distraught families, she'd lived through her own desolation, yet she couldn't bear to see that look in Josh's eyes.

"It doesn't fit." The words broke past the barricade she'd tried to hastily put up. None of her walls could hold against him, it seemed. "The dollar amount would be much higher, in the millions, if it was money at all."

"Enough to cripple the company and stop the Eureka?"

She nodded, glad to see that the pain had receded and that his mind was back to its normal quickness. This newfound strength of his seemed to be holding up well, even in the face of the unexpected curve thrown at him this morning.

"More likely it would be a direct demand that you stop production, with maybe a flight to safety thrown in." She studied him for a moment. "It would be a tough decision," she said tentatively.

"The hell it would."

His voice was flat, yet full somehow of a deadly intent. She had a sudden vision of him going against his very essence and buckling to the demands of a barbarous, bloodthirsty terrorist for the sake of his son. And once he had his son back—or if anything happened to that son—she wouldn't give a nickel for the life of any of them. She had seen Josh Kincaid's eyes.

She managed to put it out of her mind later, when she sat at the desk looking at the mass of paper in front of her. She had spent nearly two hours at the computer terminal, running every license plate in her notes through the Department of Motor Vehicles. She picked up the stack of printed results, thankful at least that none of them had thrown her completely off stride by turning up stolen.

Most of them went into one stack off to the side when they came back registered at the houses they'd been parked at. The few out-of-state ones went into two stacks, rental cars separate. The ones registered in Orange County but not Aliso Beach also went in two different stacks: those in neighboring cities, and those farther away. Then she pulled out those in southern California but outside Orange County, then those left from elsewhere in the state.

She looked at the chaos rather grimly; when Victor Curtis came back, he wasn't going to be happy. So you'd better be done and out of here before he does, Garrett, she told herself, and reached for the biggest stack.

She further divided the Aliso Beach stack—did anybody in this town not own an expensive sedan, she wondered? Sure, she answered her own question. The ones who owned sports cars. Or old pickups, she added to herself, smiling without even realizing it.

After setting aside all those vehicles that had been registered to people she'd already spoken to, she made a list of the few she hadn't. After she'd combined the multiple cars most of these people seemed to own, her pile was considerably smaller.

Ah, yes, she said as she yawned and stretched some time later, the glory of being a detective. Paperwork, legwork, ridiculous hours... She thought suddenly of the bumper sticker that Sam Singer had bought for her, daring her to put it on her car. Crime

Doesn't Pay, it had declared. But, Then, Neither Does Police Work. She had laughed and done it, but her lieutenant had not been amused.

Her lieutenant. Oh, damn, she thought. She hadn't checked in with him yesterday. He would be livid, she knew; he liked having people call him wanting to borrow his prize investigator, but he did not like being left out of her chain of command. She reached for the phone.

Livid was not a strong-enough word. Lieutenant Lindsay was furious. After the expected harangue about maintaining proper contact with him— "You do, after all, work for *us*, if you remember,"—he began making irate noises about how long she'd been on this case.

"Yes, sir, but I'm afraid things have changed drastically within the last thirty-six hours. It's an entirely new case."

"Then they can get an entirely new investigator to work it."

"But I'm already into it, sir. I have the feel of it—I've done all the groundwork."

"Yet." It was sour, but less angry. "What about this supposed terrorist angle?"

"There's no evidence to support it at this time," she said carefully.

"Then there's no need for your expertise, is there?"

Damn, she thought again. She should have guessed that he would be intrigued by the possibility of a high-profile case.

"My expertise is with missing children, not Khaddafi's latest export."

"And you could be using it here. We have cases of our own, you know."

"And I'll be on them as soon as I wind this up." She couldn't quit, not now. She couldn't abandon Josh. She wouldn't abandon Josh.

"But you don't know when that will be." Lindsay said sternly. "I agreed to your consulting on this case because of the importance of Josh Kincaid. I didn't intend for you to take it over."

"I didn't, either. But I have a rapport with him now—"

"So I gathered from the news reports. I presume you were that 'unidentified female companion'?"

Damn, she thought for the third time. What else could go wrong?

"I want you off the case and back here. Today."

That, she muttered silently.

"I can't do that, sir."

"I beg your pardon? That was an order, Hunter."

"I can't quit now. You've always taught us to see things through to the end—"

"You have," he interrupted. "This is the end. You're recalled, Garrett."

She took a deep breath. Jim Lindsay was generally a reasonable person, but sometimes his by-the-book tendencies crept out. She knew she was on very thin ice here, and the wrong words could send her crashing through.

"All right," she said slowly.

"All right?" He sounded skeptical.

"Yes. By the way, do you remember that vacation you've been nagging at me to take?"

"The one you haven't taken in five and a half years? Of course."

"I'd like it now."

"Now? What are— Oh, no, you don't. I said you're off the case. You've spent more than enough time on it. If they can't take what you've done and finish it themselves, that's their problem."

No, it's Jason Kincaid's problem. "Do I get it or not?"

"Hunter—"

"I have over sixty days coming. Are you saying I can't take them?"

"No, but—"

"Good. I wouldn't want to have to file a grievance."

There was a moment of silence, and Hunter thought she had pushed him too far. I don't care, she thought recklessly. I'm not walking away from this now. Not until Jason is back home.

And then? The question rose to haunt her, and she shoved it aside. She didn't want to think about that now, about the time when she would have to walk away, when Josh would no longer be a part of her life. She yanked her attention back to the phone in time to hear Lindsay's words.

"It's that important to you?"

"Yes, sir. It is."

Another pause. "All right," he said at last, "but hurry it up, will you? I can't justify spending the country's money too much longer."

"Thank you," Hunter said with relief. She'd meant what she'd said, but she knew her action would have strained what had been until now a very easy working relationship. But Jim had come through once again, putting people ahead of "the book."

"That was quite a bluff."

Sam's voice coming from the doorway startled her, and her head snapped up. He was looking at her rather oddly, and she knew he'd heard enough to guess the substance of the conversation.

"I wasn't bluffing."

"I was afraid of that."

Hunter's brow furrowed as she looked at him. "What does that mean?"

"Nothing." He walked into the office. "You've been up and at it early, I see."

"Yeah." She grimaced at the cluttered desk. "Nothing like starting over to brighten your morning."

"Not quite over."

She looked back up at him; that strange expression was back on his face. "What?"

"I mean, you already know Kincaid."

"What are you trying to say, Sam?"

"Just that I've known you for a long time, and I've never seen you so wrapped up before."

"It's an unusual case. And it just got a lot more complicated."

"That's not what I meant."

Hunter sighed. "Then perhaps you'd better tell me exactly what you *do* mean, Sam."

"I mean you're getting awfully involved with Josh Kincaid."

Hunter's cheeks flamed. She knew it, and it made her angry, which only aggravated the problem. "Been listening to the news, Sam?" she said icily.

He had the grace to flush. "Yes, but that's not—I've seen it myself, Hunter, and then that thing this morning..."

Hunter stood up behind the desk, tossing down her pencil. "And exactly what do you mean by 'that thing' this morning?"

"You weren't here last night. I stopped by."

"And?"

"And you were at Kincaid's at six this morning."

"Thank you for pointing that out."

Her voice was at chilly odds with her hot cheeks. She knew what he was thinking, and it only made her remember the hours spent tossing and turning, knowing she was only feet away from Josh's room, and from his bed. And it made her remember the dreams. The hot, steamy, erotic dreams, unlike anything she'd ever experienced before. Josh, coming to her, making long, sweet love to her, touching her in a way she'd never been touched, fueling the fire she'd never guessed existed inside her until he'd kissed her.

She had to stop thinking like this! Her feelings were confused enough; there was no way Josh could be thinking straight. He might think he wanted her, but his life was in such turmoil right now, he couldn't be truly sure of anything.

She focused suddenly on Sam and realized from his look that her own turmoil must be evident in her face.

"I'm sorry, Hunter," he said with a touch of sadness and regret she didn't understand. "I just don't want to see you get hurt, that's all."

She felt a rush of penitence fill her. Sam was a friend, had been a friend for a long time. He had been there for her when they'd found Timmy too late, and he'd helped her bury her husband. And she was treating him terribly, just because he had happened to innocently hit a nerve he had no idea was so sensitive.

"I'm sorry, Sam. I'm just tired, I guess. I didn't mean to jump all over you."

"I know." His voice still echoed with the reluctant tone of a man who's had his worst fears confirmed. Then he seemed to shake it off. "What can I do to help?"

Knock some sense into me, she thought, although she knew he meant with the pile on the desk. I wish it could be that easy. That I could just shake myself and forget that Josh Kincaid is the most incredible man I've ever met. Forget those blue eyes and those damn soft eyelashes. Forget that body and that mouth. Forget that he's who and what he is. Forget what he can do to me. Forget him.

By comparison the task before her seemed simple.

Chapter 11

She had expected an inner battle when she pulled into the Kincaid Industries parking lot; she hadn't expected the deluge of sweet, hot memories that washed over her as she drove past the site of that fevered kiss. The only thing that enabled her to control her reaction at all was remembering the last time she had gone into this building, the night she had thought it was all over.

Josh could have, perhaps even should have, hated her for that. Yet he hadn't, and she marveled yet again at the change in him. Sometimes you only know how much guilt has incapacitated you when it is gone and you feel the difference, she thought.

Josh's truck had not been in that same spot, nor had it been in the spot that was marked with his name. She got her first hint as to why when she saw the cluster of people outside the lobby doors. The vultures had descended, she thought; there were three times the number of reporters here than there had been this morning.

Carefully keeping her distance, she drove around to the back of the building, searching for another entrance. She saw a sign for deliveries and janitorial service, and headed for it. And couldn't help smiling when she saw, parked blatantly blocking the service entrance, the now-familiar old truck. He learns fast, she mused silently.

This, she thought when she at last stood in his office doorway, is what my brain has been resembling lately. Utter chaos.

There were at least eight people in the room, all with hands full of papers, blueprints and notepads. Josh was standing behind his desk, on two phones at once, carrying on both conversations at once while snapping out instant answers to whatever the other occupants of the room were asking him.

Hunter just stood there and watched. This was the man, she thought, that had built this business, this building. This was the man from that picture in the newsmagazine, the man who had taken on impossible odds without a second's hesitation. And won.

She would have thought, in the elegance of this office, that his casual clothes would have seemed out of place. But nothing, she realized, could take away from the aura of power he carried with him. In that moment she realized just how much that helplessness of feeling that he was responsible for Jason's disappearance must have eaten at him. *Helpless* was a word that never would be applied to the Josh Kincaid she was seeing now.

But it seems to describe me well enough, she thought ruefully when she realized her eyes had focused on the front of his shirt while her mind willingly supplied a vivid memory of the bare, muscled chest beneath it.

Josh was in the midst of snapping out an order to a nodding young man in a three-piece suit who stood beside him when he looked up and saw her. He stopped dead, midsentence, staring as if he'd never seen her before. Or as if he could read her thoughts, she thought, blushing. And to Hunter's embarrassment, every person in the office turned to see what had stopped their dynamic boss in his tracks.

"Check with Maria in accounting—she has the figures on that," Josh, recovering, said to the three-piece suit before turning to the woman who was holding a clipboard out to him. He quickly signed the bottom and handed it back to her as he spoke into one of the phone receivers.

"That's the best I can do. I'll let you know if I can change it from tentative to definite." He paused, listening. "No, I can't. Not until this is resolved."

He hung up that phone and spoke into the other.

"Yes, I know it's next month. I said it will be done, and it will. I have good people here." He gave a nod to the one note thrust in front of him by the woman Hunter knew was his secretary, then put his hand over the phone's mouthpiece to say "Tell him I'll call him back'' to the second message she showed him. Then back to the phone.

''I realized I said I would be there. It can't be helped.'' Another pause, then he spoke again, his voice icy. ''No. It is *not* negotiable.'' He hung up abruptly.

''Josh, those people are still downstairs,'' said a rather harried-looking Oriental man of about forty. ''They're really giving Sarah a hard time. She's trying to hold them off, but it's getting difficult.''

''Where's Miguel?''

''Still working on that statement you asked for.''

''Tell him to step on it, will you, Tran? We need to get them out of here, and I want to go over it with Investigator Garrett before I release it.''

The man nodded, stole a quick glance at Hunter, then hurried out as Hunter wondered if Josh had really hesitated over using her rank instead of just her name.

Quickly he dispensed with the rest of the room's occupants, answering questions and giving instructions with a speed and clarity that had to be part of the reason for the respect they so clearly gave him.

When the last one had left, closing the door carefully, Josh let out a breath and turned to look at her.

''Hi.''

''Hi. Pretty impressive, Mr. Chief Executive.''

He made a wry face. ''Sometimes I wish I was back digging ditches. At least it was—''

The intercom on his desk interrupted him, and he pushed the button roughly. ''What is it, Mary?''

''Mr. Nguyen with the press release for you.''

''Okay, send him in.''

The same man she had seen before entered with a sheet of paper covered with lines of words scrawled in red ink. He nodded to Hunter, then handed the paper to Josh. No sooner had he taken it than the phone rang. Josh let out an exasperated breath and grabbed the phone.

''You are the Investigator Garrett who is handling young Jason's kidnapping?'' Mr. Nguyen asked.

She nodded.

''A terrible thing. I have never seen Josh like this. But he has a great deal of faith in you.''

She tried to ignore the rush of pleasure his words gave her. She looked at him curiously. ''You've known him a long time?''

"Many years. He gave me a job when I came to this country, when few would even speak to me. And when I wished to bring my family here, he sponsored them. I owe him much."

Hunter's eyes swung back to Josh. Would he never cease to surprise her? He hung up, scribbled a quick note on a pad that was already nearly full, then raised his head. He caught her bemused expression and stared at her quizzically.

"Mr. Nguyen is waiting," she said hastily.

"Call me Tran, please." The man gave her a slight bow before handing the paper he held to Josh. "Miguel is still up to his neck in phone calls, so I brought this for him."

Josh scanned the paper quickly. "Give us a few minutes with it," he said to Tran. "I'll ship it back to Miguel with any changes, and he can go ahead."

When they were alone, he handed her the page of red ink and she sat down to read it. It took her a moment to learn the style of the writing which seemed to include multiple *R*s that looked like *S*s, but she soon saw that it was a nicely worded press release that denied any terrorist connection to the disappearance of the son of the CEO of Kincaid Industries, and stated unequivocally that the production of the Eureka II was in no way affected.

"I worried about planting the idea in the minds of those who hadn't thought of it already," he said when he saw she'd finished, "but it seems those charmers that were there this morning have made sure it's occurred to everyone by now."

"Yes," she thought, remembering the rather furtive stares she'd got en masse from the Aliso Beach detectives when she'd left the office. She knew several of them from their days with the sheriff's office before they'd elected to come over when this department had been formed. A couple had even, after Dan's death, asked her out. She had invariably declined, and she could almost read the speculation in their faces now.

"Well, I hope that will hold them for a while."

"Not for long," she warned.

"I know. I just need some breathing room." He grimaced. "I don't much like being held prisoner in my own building."

Hunter smiled at him. "I saw you used the servant's entrance."

"Yeah." She saw his mouth twitch. "They never even looked at my poor old truck."

"Judging a book by its cover," she teased. "Always a bad idea."

"Unless you discover that the inside is even more interesting than the outside."

There was no particular emphasis in his voice, but something about the way he was looking at her as he said those words made her cheeks heat.

"This has to be changed," she said abruptly. She hadn't meant to sound so blunt or authoritative, but he answered mildly enough.

"What?"

She took a breath and tried again. "I just meant that this needs to be deleted." She held it out to him, indicating the line she was referring to with a slender finger. "No details on the date or the time. Or the fact that the sheriff's office is involved at all. We don't want to spook him by making him think the whole county's after him. It might make him too careful, and we need him to make a mistake."

"All right." He took the paper and scratched out the offending lines. "How about 'local authorities'?" He grinned suddenly, unexpectedly. "I'd like to throw their own euphemisms back at them."

When she could breathe, Hunter nodded. Lord, that grin took her breath away! She was seized with a sudden longing to see him like that all the time, free of the weight he was carrying, free of the nightmare.

"You look pretty busy here," she said hurriedly, still disconcerted by the strength of her reactions to him.

"It's piled up a little."

"Why don't you finish? I'll let you know if anything turns up."

He looked from the stacks of papers demanding his attention, glanced at the phone that was blinking madly with lines on hold, then back to her.

"Unless, of course," she said lightly, "you've become addicted to futility, and want to pound the pavement for nothing for a few more hours."

What I've become addicted to, Josh thought, is you. Even the thought of all he had to do wasn't enough to match the attraction of spending the afternoon with her, doing anything. Besides, even the slightest change that they might come across something that would help find Jason was enough to make him throw his work to the wind.

Hunter read the changes in his expression and said softly, "I can do the legwork, Josh. Nobody else—" she gestured at his cluttered desk "—can do *this*."

He sat down abruptly, an angry exclamation breaking from him. "I just..." He trailed off, his frustration evident in his eyes.

"I know. It's so horribly hard to wait. But really, until Saturday all there is to do is miles of legwork with a very slim chance of getting lucky and finding something."

He picked up a pencil from amid the clutter on his desk, then tossed it back down. Hunter wanted to tell him to ignore everything she'd said, to come with her, but she beat down the urge. She had work to do, and judging from her concentration level whenever he was around, it would get done much more efficiently without him. She made herself go on.

"Get caught up here, Josh. You may not have much time after Saturday. I've seen those goons run people ragged with their little games. They like to see people jump when they talk. Especially people like you."

"Like me?"

"People who don't jump for anyone."

I seem to jump for you, he thought wryly. Then something else occurred to him. "You think it's someone who knows me? At least enough to...think that?"

She looked surprised, then thoughtful. "Yes, I guess I do."

"Why?"

"I'm not sure. Somehow it just all seems connected." She gave a little laugh. "I'm not being very definite, am I? I just get the feeling it's local."

"Good enough for me."

"That's it? Just like that?"

He shrugged. "Somebody told me once to trust the experts." Hunter felt her cheeks heat again as he quoted her words. Damn, she had to stop doing this every time she saw him! She got up hastily.

"You'll wait, then? I'll call if—"

The intercom buzzed again; Josh's hand shot out to snap it on in a movement sharp with annoyance.

"I'm sorry, Mr. Kincaid, but John Lowell is on line two—he says he has a crisis. Paul Naguchi is on three, and Wayne Collins from the Association of Airport Administrators called. He's very anxious to talk to you." Her voice was apologetic. "He's heard the news and he's very concerned."

Josh sucked in a long breath.

"Oh, and Mrs. Webb wants an appointment—she's flying in this afternoon. I've pulled her reports for you to review. And those letters are ready for your signature."

He let the breath out sharply from between compressed lips. His eyes flickered to Hunter. She read the weary resignation in his eyes as he told Mary to hold everything for a minute.

"Do what you have to do," she said softly.

"What I have to do," he repeated. He smiled, a crooked little twist of his mouth that was decidedly humorless. "It used to be all I wanted to do."

"Nothing like a heavy dose of cold reality to rearrange your priorities."

"Is that what happened to you?" He said it softly, the sudden change in his voice to that almost caressing tone sending that little shiver up her spine again. She was so intent on trying to keep it in check that she answered without thinking.

"It changed my life. I thought for a while it had ended it." Her head came up suddenly. "You'll get Jason back," she said fiercely, her voice catching in her throat. "You will. I won't see you go through that."

Josh clenched his jaw against the tide of feeling that rose in him at her intensity, at the fire in her eyes as she looked at him and at the barely perceptible emphasis she put in the "you" in that last sentence.

She doesn't mean anything by it, he told himself desperately. It's her work she's so passionate about, not you. Then he swore silently at himself for the images he'd brought on by using the word passionate in conjunction with Hunter. His sudden need for distance between them tipped the scales, and he stood up as abruptly as she had.

"I'll walk you out."

She nodded in acceptance of his decision, turned and walked toward the office door. He was right behind her and reached around her to open the door.

"—sorry, but Mr. Kincaid is not seeing *anyone* today." Mary Spencer's voice was firm yet polite as she spoke to someone just out of their sight. "Especially without an appointment."

Hunter smothered a smile; the slightest touch of English upper crust had crept into Josh's secretary's voice. It was an amazing weapon, causing many people to be intimidated without ever realizing why. Although the woman had left her native London years ago and had worked for Josh for ten years, she had never forgotten how to use that regal voice to her advantage.

"She does that so well, doesn't she?" Josh whispered archly. "Remind me to give her a raise."

Hunter giggled. She couldn't help it, nor could she help the need that rose in her again to see him like this all the time instead of in brief, fleeting flashes. Then, as they stepped into the outer office, she felt him suddenly stiffen.

"Son of a—" He cut off his muttered oath, then strode across the room angrily. "What are you doing up here?"

Hunter groaned inwardly when she saw that the man he was glaring at was the beady-eyed, stocky reporter who had been at the house. At something in his eyes the man took a half step back, then laughed as if to make a joke of this instinctive retreat. Hunter hurried over, wondering if she was going to need any of those black-belt talents to keep the peace here.

"You really *do* know this man, Mr. Kincaid?" Mary asked in surprise.

Josh didn't miss the implication. He held the man pinned with those riveting eyes as he answered her question with another.

"Did he say I did?"

"Yes. He said you were old friends and he'd come to see if there was anything he could do...."

"But you didn't believe him?"

"Well," Mary said doubtfully, "I couldn't quite see him as a friend of yours, I must admit. If I'm wrong, then I apol—"

"You weren't wrong." His gaze flicked to Hunter. "Remind me to make that a large raise."

Hunter let out the breath she'd been unconsciously holding. She saw the fury in his eyes, but saw also that while he might be enraged at this second trespass into his private domain, he was also in control. Barely.

"Get out," he said icily, turning back to the shorter man, "and if I ever catch you within throwing distance of me again, I'll—"

"Get a restraining order against you," Hunter cut in smoothly before Josh could make a threat that could get him into trouble. "There is a press release that will be made available downstairs shortly, Mr. Baldwin. And that is all that will be available for now. I suggest you content yourself with that."

"Mr. Baldwin?" the round man said, eyebrows raised. "I see you've done your homework, young lady. Or should I say, Deputy Garrett?"

Damn, Hunter, thought inwardly; her face remained impassive.

"I knew I'd seen you somewhere before. It just took a trip through the back files of the local papers to place you. The missing-person whiz herself."

Hunter ignored him as if he hadn't spoken. "There is nothing for you here, Mr. Baldwin. Goodbye."

"Going to arrest me for trespassing?" He smirked.

"Mr. Kincaid owns this building. If he wishes to make a citizen's arrest for trespassing, I would be delighted to assist."

"*Mr.* Kincaid?" The smirk again. "Funny, somehow I got the idea you two were...much closer than that."

Hunter felt Josh go rigid then take one quick stride forward, coming up hard against the shorter man's pudgy body. "You little—"

"Josh, no."

"I'm throwing them all the hell out of here."

When fear flickered for the first time in the reporter's eyes, Hunter felt no hesitation in grabbing Josh and pulling him away from the other man.

"That's just what he wants. You take a swing at him, and he winds up on the front page."

She had succeeded in diverting Josh, at least for the moment. She turned back to Baldwin.

"I'll give you that front page, Mr. Baldwin."

The beady eyes blinked, startled. "What?"

"You want headlines, you'll get them. *After* the boy is safe." She felt Josh move, but didn't look at him. She was intent on the rotund reporter. "Anything you print about my involvement beforehand endangers that child's life."

"But—"

"You know I could go to your editor, and he'd put the lid on." The other things she'd rather do to muzzle this beast went through her mind, but she concentrated on salvaging a bad situation. "But if you'll cooperate now, by keeping this quiet until Mr. Kincaid's son is safe and spreading the word to your colleagues that there's nothing to be gained by this...vigil, the story's yours afterwards."

"What?" Josh's sharp exclamation made Baldwin jump, but Hunter never wavered.

"What do you say, Mr. Baldwin?"

"First?" The tiny, bright eyes were gleaming now.

"First. And you'll get all the credit."

He hesitated, and Hunter read his distrust. "I mean it, Mr. Baldwin. I don't make idle promises."

"So I've heard." The balding head nodded abruptly. "All right. You've got a deal."

His gaze flickered to Josh, who was staring at Hunter with a look in his steel blue eyes that made the corpulent reporter scurry out like a man unsure of a safe escape.

Josh grabbed Hunter by one arm and tugged her forcefully out into the now-empty hall and slammed the door shut behind them.

"How could you make a deal with that—"

"I had no choice. The last thing we need is the world knowing that I've been called in on this."

"He was the one that was going to drag you through the mud!"

"I know."

"Then why the hell didn't I just throw him out of here? Damn it, Hunter, it—"

"It isn't going to do anybody any good to deliberately antagonize them."

"Antagonize them? It's my son who's been kidnapped—why the hell should I give a damn about antagonizing *them?*"

"Josh, I've dealt with them ever since I've been a cop. They really aren't all like Baldwin. They don't all lose all decency in their drive for a story...."

Her voice caught, and Josh felt a pang deep inside as he remembered that she probably knew better than most exactly what a rabid press was capable of. But before he could speak, she had recovered.

"Most of them try to do a good job, but they look at things differently. And we have to handle it. It's much better if you can keep them objective, if not on your side. They're a fact of life."

"So are rattlesnakes, but that doesn't mean I'm nice to them."

He said it dryly, a bit sourly, but not angrily, and Hunter knew with relief that the storm had passed. For now. She wondered how many other pressures he could absorb without breaking. Even Josh Kincaid had to have limits.

"Don't be nice. Civil will do. Just stay cool, and don't give them any ammunition."

He sighed. "I seem to be running a little short of cool lately."

"You're worried to death about Jason."

"Yeah." I could handle that better, he thought, if I didn't have to work so hard to keep that cool around you.

She studied him for a moment, wondering what was behind that odd look in his eyes. "Are you all right?"

He chuckled harshly. "Me? Sure."

I'm just going nuts, he muttered silently. Jason is God knows where, probably scared, maybe hurt, this woman is his only hope, and what do I do? I go into an early mid-life crisis over her. He pulled his scattered thoughts together.

"I'd better get down and hustle Miguel up with that press release."

"I'd better get going, too," she said. Then she looked back over her shoulder as she turned to go. "Did they call you about the welfare hearing for Rob Barrington on Friday?"

"Yeah, I've got a message about it somewhere on my desk."

"I know it's awfully soon, but I guess Barrington, Sr.'s, name throws some weight in high circles." Almost as much as yours, she thought. "And since it's only a hearing to decide about counseling for Rob, thanks to you, they agreed."

Josh shrugged, as if to dismiss his own generosity as negligible.

Hunter was silent for a long moment before she said quietly, "I...admire your strength, Josh."

Something flashed in the blue eyes, hot and alive. Then he let out a long, sighing breath. "Right now I don't feel very strong."

"That's what I mean. Even when you don't feel strong, you keep going."

He felt absurdly warmed by her words, but wary at the same time. "Don't make me out to be a hero or something."

"What's a hero besides somebody who keeps going when others stop?"

"Somebody who's too dumb to know when he's licked?" he suggested solemnly. "Or just too tired."

Tired. She knew about that, she thought, even as she smiled at his words. After the night that was supposed to be one of rest had turned into one of hot, restless longing, she knew all too much about it. "Dreams," she muttered.

"What?"

"Nothing," she said, flustered. "Just something about...dreams. And heroes." How true her hasty explanation was, she thought ruefully.

He quirked an eyebrow at her. "I am also too tired to deal with enigmatic Garrett observations."

She flushed then, muttered a hasty goodbye and fled down the hall. She managed to occupy her mind by making the threat of being discovered by the other members of the media who were milling about much larger than it was. Keeping out of their way kept her thoughts obedient, at least until she was out of the building and back in her car.

She tried then to block them out with the mechanical motions of driving, giving every command to signal, brake and turn as if she'd just driven away from DMV with a brand-new license. It didn't work.

Keep this up, and you'll cause an accident, she told herself severely. She pulled over into a small shopping-center parking lot and stopped the car, knowing she had to face some things she'd been avoiding.

Did she really do that? Did she really play up the—what had Josh called it?—the "Garrett mystique"?

She supposed, without any real conceit, that there was such a thing. She'd heard about it enough, in glowing introductions at the classes she'd taught, and at a few ceremonies that had resulted in the awards that graced her office walls. And Sam had constantly teased her, albeit affectionately, about her widespread reputation.

Had she let it go to her head? Had she lost sight of why she was in this work? She sat very still, her hands clenched around the steering wheel, trying as she hadn't had to in a long time to be brutally honest with herself. She didn't like what she saw.

It was true. She wanted to deny it, to write it off to an overwrought reaction from a man stressed to the limit, but it wouldn't work. As she had just seen, if anything, Josh's mind got sharper under pressure. Besides, now that he had made her take a close look, she could see it for herself.

She had liked it, she thought miserably. Liked it that her mind seemed to work a little more agilely, a little faster than others. She had begun to take pride in the fact that people couldn't understand why she was usually right, or how she got there. She had, she realized, begun to take credit for what was in reality an instinct she had little to do with except to feed it the necessary information.

You, she told herself, have let your ego get out of hand. You're as bad as an actor who starts believing his own publicity. You've got so wrapped up in admiring your own methods that you've forgotten the goal.

Her silent castigation continued for a long time. It was an unpleasant moment of self-revelation, but she had never been one to avoid facing the truth, even when painful. Except, she thought grimly, when you manage to avoid seeing it at all until someone makes you take a closer look.

Josh. He had seen what the people she worked with everyday hadn't. Yet Tran had said he had faith in her. And Josh was very, very smart. If he believed in her, he must have reason. He didn't give his trust easily. So there must still be something there to trust, mustn't there?

Her faith in herself had never been so shaken. No matter what else had happened in her life, she had always had the vital, central core of her work to get her through. When everything else was falling down around her, she still had that one kernel of comfort, the knowledge that she was very good at what she did. A knowledge that, it appeared now, had swollen to peacock proportions.

She shuddered as she remembered a night long ago, when her shattered husband had screamed that it was all her fault, that if she hadn't been so involved with her damn job, Timmy would still be alive.

With the swiftness of long practice, she shrugged off the memory. Yes, her work had taken her away a lot, but it had also, with its odd hours, given her as much if not more time with her son than other working mothers had. It wasn't true, she told herself.

But the rest was. And it had taken Josh to make her see it. She had some changes to make, starting now. And with the determination that had seen her through tragedy, she formed a solemn resolution that never again would she forget the true reason for her commitment to her work.

Chapter 12

Josh paced the hallway restlessly. He knew he was early, and even admitted ruefully that he was early because he had hoped to see Hunter before the hastily scheduled hearing for Rob Barrington began. He hadn't seen her since that day she had hurried out of his building, and he was hungry for the sight of her. That fact, however, was beyond his capacity to admit, so he shoved it aside into that spot in his mind that had never been so crowded until Hunter.

She had called a couple of times to let him know there were no new developments. He tried to jeer at himself for the way his heart sped up the moment he heard her voice, but his self-derision hadn't been very effective. He turned as he reached the end of the hall outside the hearing room and started back.

Each time after hanging up he had sat in rueful silence, acknowledging how she had managed to ease his turmoil with just her silky voice and soft words. He was still so torn, feeling guilty that he wasn't doing something concrete about finding Jason yet knowing that if he didn't put some time in at his office, the whole place was going to come down around his ears. He'd been running nonstop since he'd come in that morning, had done some couch sleeping of his own, and he had to admit it at least distracted him a little from the ever-present pain and apprehension.

He reached the intersecting hallway at the other end of the one he was pacing and pivoted automatically for the return journey. She had sounded tired the last time, he thought with concern. She was pushing so hard, and—

"—dare you say I don't care!"

"You don't give a damn!"

The strident voices were coming from just around the corner, and he was about to quicken his pace to give the obviously agitated pair some privacy when something about that first voice stopped him. It was harsh, strident...and young. Rob Barrington.

"Don't you swear at me, you little punk!"

"Yeah, that's it, Dad. Tell the world what you think of your worthless son."

Bitterness, harsh and corrosive as acid, rang in Rob's young voice. Josh held his breath, his heart pounding. He tried desperately to keep the years from spinning away, back to a time when it had been himself standing before the cold, forbidding figure of his father, yelling similar words with that same tortured note in his voice.

"You are worthless," the older man shouted, careless of who might hear. "You've got every damn thing in the world, and you still do your best to embarrass me every chance you get! Get inside and sit down. I don't want another word out of you." There was a rustling, a yelp of protest, then the slamming of a door.

Josh sagged against the wall behind him, taking in deep breaths to slow his hammering pulse. Dominoes, he thought inanely. His father to him. Rob's father to him. And ...himself to Jason.

With a sudden, convulsive movement he straightened up, then walked with swift purpose toward the door of the hearing room.

"Ed Sterling is out of town, and the pitcher, ah—" Sam consulted his notepad as they hurried down the hall "—Dirk, hasn't been around. I'll have to catch him later. But so far, nobody knows anything. Except that Rob is in deep trouble with his old man."

Hunter already knew that. It hadn't been hard to deduce from the boy's sullen attitude when he found out his father was returning from New York and had demanded that this hearing be held today.

"The whole world jumps to his tune," he'd said caustically. "Why should the law be any different?"

Hunter's heart had gone out to the confused, angry teenager; in spite of everything, she couldn't convince herself that he had truly meant any harm. And she was thankful anew that Josh had found it in himself to at least understand, if not forgive, this troubled boy.

She heard the chime of a clock somewhere in the building and picked up the pace even more. She didn't want to get chewed out by the hearing officer any more than she already would be.

"Don't be in such a rush," Sam said. "Wagner's been in a meeting since I got here."

"A meeting?"

"Yeah. Locked up in her office with the kid." He smiled rather gleefully. "Old man Barrington's been pacing the floor ever since they called the kid in there and told him he had to wait outside."

Hunter couldn't help echoing his smile. "I'll bet he's not used to being kept cooling his heels."

The man in question was still pacing as they went into the room. His eyes flicked over them as they came in, dismissed them, then, as if in sudden reconsideration, returned to give Hunter a more detailed inspection. Something in his gaze made her skin crawl, and she had to force herself not to look away hastily.

He was barely taller than she was, she noticed, and at least an inch shorter than his son. Fleshy rather than fat, his graying hair was carefully styled, his suit blatantly expensive. A heavy gold bracelet circled one chubby wrist, and a thick, nugget-textured gold watch adorned the other.

She found herself comparing this display to the discreet elegance of Josh's thin, gold watch, the only outward evidence of his wealth. Of course, she thought, his looks were ornament enough; that body didn't need any gilding.

Stop it, she ordered herself.

"Mr. Barrington?" Christine Wagner, the juvenile hearing officer, stood in the doorway of the small office at the back of the room. "Would you come in for a moment, please?"

The man turned and gave the woman a glare, waiting just long enough to show her he wasn't impressed by her authority. Power struggle, Hunter thought suddenly, remembering that first day with Josh. Except this man would never have the grace nor the class to admit that that was what it was.

She and Sam crossed to the long table that sat at one side of the room, and she set down her case file. She glanced around as if looking for someone.

"Do you think that—"

She stopped suddenly as the sound of raised voices came from behind the closed office door. Or rather, one voice. It was muffled, unintelligible, but unmistakably angry. She exchanged a glance with Sam, whose eyebrows went up quizzically.

"Didn't you say Kincaid wasn't pressing any charges?"

She nodded. "He never even considered it."

"Pretty charitable of him, considering."

"He...understands what Rob's going through. He said he's got trouble enough already, with those parents." The voices rose again behind the door.

"Then I wonder what that's all about?" Sam asked.

"I don't know." She looked around again.

"You expecting someone else?" Sam asked, a shade too casually.

She didn't bother to deny it. "Josh. He said he wanted to be here, to see what they decided to do."

As if she'd conjured him up with her words, when she turned at the sound of a door opening, there he was. Her brow furrowed when she saw that he, too, had apparently been in the meeting that had produced that loud, obstreperous reaction in Robert Barrington, Sr. What on earth? she wondered.

Mrs. Wagner, a tall, slender woman with blond hair threaded with silver, crossed the room to sit at the slightly raised dais in the front of the room. A still red-faced Robert Barrington sat in a chair to the left, obviously unhappy with whatever had transpired. Rob, on the other hand, wore an expression of stunned amazement. And he was staring at Josh in disbelief.

The object of the teenager's astonished gaze was walking, with that easy grace that sent an odd little ripple along Hunter's nerves, across the room. He saw her then, and there was just the slightest hitch in his smooth stride.

He sat in a chair next to the one Rob had taken, and Hunter had the oddest feeling that she was seeing more than just a chance selection of chairs. It was as if Josh had aligned himself with Rob, leaving the teenager's father alone with his anger.

She tried to keep her eyes fastened on the welfare officer, but it wasn't easy; she kept seeing Josh in her mind. The somber elegance of his dark suit, cut exquisitely to fit that lean, wide-shouldered body, was lightened by the pale blue of his shirt, its color emphasizing the piercing glow of his eyes. He looked strong, capable and in control, the antithesis of the choleric man who sat alone across the room.

As Mrs. Wagner called for their attention, Hunter couldn't resist a glance at him. Green eyes met penetrating blue ones and held for one long moment before they both turned their attention to the woman at the front of the room as she began to speak.

"All right, let's get started. I think we can wrap this up quickly, thanks to Mr. Kincaid's generosity."

Hunter's eyes flicked to Josh curiously. She learned nothing; he was looking steadfastly at Mrs. Wagner.

"First of all," the woman went on, her eyes fastened on a chastened-looking Rob Barrington, "I want you to realize what would have happened had you been dealing with someone less understanding than Mr. Kincaid. Since you are seventeen, you could have been arrested and tried as an adult. You would have been remanded to the California Youth Authority. Do you understand what that means?"

White-faced, Rob nodded.

"Very well." She shifted her gaze to Hunter. "Thank you for appearing here today, Investigator Garrett. I appreciate the interest you've expressed in Rob's welfare. As you are aware, Mr. Kincaid has elected not to press charges for the attempted extortion. In view of the circumstances, do you have any objection?"

"None." None at all, she thought fervently.

"This is, of course," Mrs. Wagner went on, "contingent upon the fulfillment of the conditions agreed upon in conference." Her gaze shifted to Rob. "If at any time those conditions are not satisfactorily met, you will be ordered to return to this court for a formal hearing. Do you understand?"

"Yes."

Rob's voice cracked, and Hunter saw him blush. There was no trace of the cocky kid she'd seen before. He seemed barely more than a child now, a scared one at that, and she was more than glad that Josh had found the strength to forgive—she was proud. She didn't stop to think of the implications of that.

"At this point, I see no need to have you declared a ward of the court or consider proceedings for emancipated minor status. You will be eighteen in a few months and responsible for yourself."

Rob's head came up, and he looked at Josh. Hunter saw the brief, reassuring nod he gave the boy, and her heart caught at the look of hope and tentative trust that lit the young face.

"Is there anything you'd like to say?"

Rob shook his head mutely.

"All right. We have reached an informal agreement that will be finalized and forwarded to all concerned parties." Her gaze shifted to Josh. "Again I must say, Mr. Kincaid, that you have been exceedingly generous and understanding. To be willing to help someone who has caused you a great deal of suffering and anguish is an act of kindness and compassion rare in this day and age. I believe your solution will prove beneficial to all involved."

Hunter's curiosity was raging now. She looked across the table at Josh. His eyes were lowered as if he were embarrassed by the woman's effusive praise. The twin sweeps of his dark lashes made him seem somehow vulnerable to her, while at the same time she was marveling at the inner strength it had taken for him to forgo the chance of revenge of a sort on the person who had caused him such pain. It was a potent combination, and she quickly averted her eyes before her feelings became obvious. She didn't notice the speculative look that came into Sam's eyes as he watched her.

"—is adjourned," Mrs. Wagner was saying as Hunter jerked her attention back to the proceedings. "Young man, I don't want to see you again. Investigator Garrett, my office please, in—" she glanced at her watch "—five minutes."

Hunter sighed as the woman left the dais. She was in for another lecture, she knew. She stood up, replacing the papers before her in the file folder she happily hadn't needed. Not that she would have, anyway; every detail of this particular case was burned into her mind with vivid clarity.

From the corner of her eye she saw Rob lean forward and whisper something to Josh, who nodded. The boy's father had stalked angrily out of the room the moment Mrs. Wagner had said the word "adjourned," never having spoken a word.

Hunter saw Mrs. Wagner approach Josh and begin to speak to him. She picked up the folder, then sat it back down as Rob came rather hesitantly to stand before her, shifting his feet uncomfortably.

"Uh...hi."

"Hi, Rob. Congratulations."

He flushed again. "I...er, I wanted to thank you."

She raised an eyebrow. "For what?"

Rob glanced over his shoulder at Josh, then back at her. "He told me you stuck up for me, with him, and the juvie people, too. I know he wouldn't have done it if you hadn't."

"Done what?"

"Give me a job."

Hunter gaped at him. "He...what?"

"Yeah. Didn't you know? At his office, just runnin' errands and stuff at first, after school, but if it works out..."

"You can make it work out," she encouraged through her shock. So that was why he'd been in that meeting! That Josh had done this for the boy who had put him through such hell...

"That's what he said." There was a gleam of respect in the boy's eyes. "He said if I didn't, he was gonna kick my...butt from here to Mexico."

In spite of herself Hunter laughed. "He would, too."

"Yeah, I know." He smiled, a little weakly, but a smile. "He said I have to keep a B average at school, too, or I'm back here." The boy grimaced.

"You have your work cut out for you," Hunter commiserated, smothering a grin.

"Yeah. But he said he'd help, too." His eyes brightened. "He even said there's a computer I could use at his office." Rob shifted his feet awkwardly again. "He's really not bad at all. Not like—well, anyway, I mean it was really something for him to do all that, after what I did. I might have had to go to juvie hall, or even jail."

"Yes," Hunter said softly.

He was looking at her quizzically. "You...I thought you'd be mad. Don't cops want to see people go to jail?"

"When they deserve it. I don't think you do." She narrowed her eyes at him. "Just don't make a liar out of me."

"I won't," he said fervently. "Or him, either. Nobody trusted me like that before, ever. Not my old man, not anybody. I won't let him down. Or you, either."

"Investigator Garrett? Now, please."

Mrs. Wagner's commanding tones cut off their conversation. Hunter gave an encouraging smile to Rob, then picked up her papers and moved out from behind the table.

Josh, watching from across the room, felt an echo of that little shock that had gone through him when he had come out of the office and seen her for the first time in nearly two days. She was wearing a simple black dress that made her hair seem alive with that burnished fire, and made the most of her slim yet curved figure. She looked fragile and a little pale, a paleness that made her eyes seem enormous in her delicate face. She looked, he thought with an inward sigh of resignation, stunning. And that was the answer to the question he'd posed earlier. Chic, elegant or effortlessly innocent, they were all the reality of Hunter Garrett.

He had tried not to look at her, tried to keep his attention on the proceedings, but it didn't work very well. His eyes kept straying to her, fastening on the sleek mass of her hair, falling forward as she looked at the papers before her, or to the slender hands as she moved those papers, or to the shapely legs crossed demurely at the racehorse-slim ankles.

He had watched her slide the papers back into the folder when Mrs. Wagner had finished, his eyes lingering on the lowered sweep of her lashes and the pert tip of her nose, then sliding down to the sweet curve of her lips. A hot, sudden memory of how those lips had felt beneath his, of how they had parted for him, luring him deeper under a spell he still hadn't broken, flooded him, and he felt his body tighten in immediate response.

He tore his eyes away as she rose from the table, and sucked in a deep, cooling breath. He didn't try to tell himself any longer that it was just the long period of abstinence that caused this fierce reaction; he had admitted days ago that no woman had ever been able to do this to him. Even the few words she had spoken during the brief hearing had been like a soft, warm breath against his ear, fingertips brushing up his spine.

He had been grateful when Rob had quietly asked if he thought it would be okay if he thanked her for her defense of him; it would keep her occupied for a moment while he tried to regain some of the control she seemed to turn to shreds so easily.

When Christine Wagner approached him after leaving the dais, he wondered again why she had summoned Hunter into her office. Something about the way Hunter had sighed, then squared her shoulders as if preparing for battle, had told him it wasn't good. He told himself it wasn't his business and tried to ignore that little voice that was saying that it was, just as anything to do with her was.

He'd never had such a proprietary feeling for anyone except Jason before. Somehow she had become as important in his mind, albeit in a different way, as his son. It made him uneasy. Not so much that he felt it, but that he was coming to accept it, and that it felt right. Then, as Mrs. Wagner again called for her and she began to cross the room in that damn little black dress that made his blood heat, he lost track of what he'd been worried about. And then her eyes met his, and his breath left him in a rush.

No one had ever looked at him like that in his life. Her eyes were so full of warmth and respect and something else he didn't dare try to name that he could barely breathe. The fact that she made no effort to hide it made its impact even more incredible, and his heart began to hammer in his chest.

For a long moment after she had disappeared into the office at the back of the room, he stood staring at the closed door, seemingly unable to move.

"Mr. Kincaid?"

His muscles responded then, at least enough for him to turn his head to look at Sam Singer.

"I heard what Rob said. That was quite a thing you did."

Still reeling from that ardent look, he merely shrugged. Then he swallowed heavily, trying to clear the lump in his throat enough to speak, to ask the question he hadn't been able to ask Mrs. Wagner.

"What," he finally managed to get out, "is that all about?" He gestured toward the closed office door with his thumb.

Sam shrugged. "Hunter getting her usual chewing out, I imagine."

Josh stared at the detective. "Chewing out?"

"Yeah. The courts tend not to like her methods."

"But she was right—she would have found Jason..."

Sam shrugged again. "But if you'd wanted to press charges, none of what she got from Rob during her interview could have been used. So she'll get the usual lecture about admissible evidence, confessions obtained by unorthodox and inadmissible means, that kind of thing."

"They really do that?"

He nodded. "It doesn't mean much, not really. She just gives her standard answer, that the primary goal is the safety of the victim. It's hard to argue with that."

"Then why do they?"

"It's part of the game."

Sam noted the look on Josh's face, a combination of concern and anger. He smothered an inward sigh of resignation and he saw his earlier speculation confirmed in a pair of steely blue eyes.

"She's not really in any trouble. As long as her success rate holds up, there won't be any official discipline." He glanced at the closed door. "It does wear on her a little, though."

The truth of that was clear to Josh when Hunter came out of the office. Her head was up, her delicate chin out in that defiant thrust he knew so well, but her shoulders were less square, as if burdened with a weariness she couldn't quite shake off. Yet her eyes warmed when she saw him, warmed in a way that made it suddenly hard to breathe.

Josh actually took a step toward her, only stopping when he realized he had been about to grab her and pull her into his arms, heedless of where they were and who was there. He fought down the need to embrace her, to take the weight from her, to ease the fatigue that clouded the emerald of her eyes.

"I'm glad you're still here, Mr. Kincaid," Mrs. Wagner said. "I wanted to express my sincere hopes that your son is safely returned to you soon. Investigator Garrett has updated me on the recent developments."

The woman turned to look at Sam. "I'm told that you are prepared to request a blanket search warrant for the neighborhood?"

Sam nodded. "Hun—Investigator Garrett and I have covered most of the residences within a mile radius already, and most of them have been cooperative. But we want the warrant for the rest."

God, Josh thought, no wonder she looks tired. She'd never mentioned that, had just written it off to the ubiquitous legwork.

"Judge Clark?"

"Yes. We've been in contact with him about the case. He's said he'll handle any warrants we need."

Mrs. Wagner nodded. "You should have no problem, then. He'll put the child's best interest first. I wish you luck. And keep me posted, please."

After she'd gone, there was a moment of awkward silence before Sam, looking at Hunter, spoke in a tone that was oddly apologetic.

"Don't forget you need to pick up the order okaying the trap on the pay phone so the guys can set it up this afternoon."

Hunter glanced at her watch, but before she could reply, Josh spoke. His voice had a sharp edge.

"You're going to go ahead and tap the phone booth?"

Hunter nodded silently. When she didn't speak, she saw something flicker in Josh's eyes and realized she was doing it again. The Garrett mystique. Lord, it was worse than she'd thought, she said to herself ruefully. Trying to keep her color from rising, she explained quickly.

"If he's watching, all he'll see is the usual janitorial service that always comes in on Friday afternoons. One of them will just happen to use the phone."

Josh still looked uneasy, and Sam put in quickly, "We'll be around in case he is in close, but we don't want to spook him."

"Even if you could catch him?"

Josh asked it as if he wasn't quite certain they would pass up a chance for an arrest.

"'Garrett's law,'" Sam said with a grin. "First rule is, the bad guy walks until the victim is safe."

Hunter couldn't halt the blush this time.

"Stop it." Her voice was a little sharp; "Garrett's law" sounded a little too close to "Garrett mystique." Sam looked at her, startled by her tone. "I'd better get over and pick up that order," she said abruptly, and turned to go.

Sam seemed taken aback by her quick movement, and it was a moment before he called to her.

"You're going to cover the phone call?"

She turned back. "Yes." Her eyes went to Josh. "I'll contact you later."

Before Josh could do more than wonder what had upset her, she was gone. But he knew something had; there had been something strangely akin to embarrassment in her eyes in those last moments. What he didn't know, couldn't imagine, was the reason for it. He wanted to follow her to find out, and more importantly find out about that look she'd given him earlier, but she'd made it clear with her abrupt departure she didn't want company.

I'll never understand that woman, Josh thought in bemusement. But I'd like to spend about the next fifty years trying. The words hung there in his mind, and no matter how hard he tried to call them back, they wouldn't go. He swore silently, then hastened to cover his reaction to his own thoughts.

"What was that about?" he asked Sam.

"The call tomorrow. The trace takes some time, even with computers these days."

With Hunter gone, Josh's mind seemed to regain its normal function, and he caught Sam's inference swiftly.

"How long do I have to keep him talking?"

Sam registered his quick grasp of the situation, and a glimmer of reluctant appreciation showed briefly in his eyes.

"It depends on how far away he's calling from." Sam smiled wryly. "As long as possible is a safe bet. Hunter will go over some stalling tactics with you before then. She's good with those."

Josh stared, wondering if there had been a double meaning in the man's words. Sam's face revealed nothing, but there was an odd glitter in his eyes.

"If she has time," Josh said, recovering. "She hasn't stopped at all, has she?"

"No." Sam looked at him, considering, then, as if he'd reached a decision, he went on. "No thanks to her boss."

"What?"

"They had quite a go-round about it the other day. I heard her half of the conversation. He wanted her off the case."

Off the case? God, Josh thought, he couldn't even begin to imagine what it would be like to go through with this without her. They couldn't pull her off, not now.

"Why?" he choked out.

"She's only on loan. They've got things piling up there, and he thought she'd been gone long enough. He wanted her to turn it all over to us and come back."

"But she's not...is she?" Josh could barely get it out.

"She backed him down. Told him she either stayed or took the five-and-a-half years' worth of vacation she has coming to her."

"Vacation?" Josh looked blank for a moment, then his eyes widened as realization dawned. "You mean she would have kept on, on her own?"

Sam nodded. Josh stared at the other man numbly.

"Isn't that...above and beyond the call?"

"It is," Sam affirmed. "Even for Hunter."

"But why?"

"Don't you know?"

Josh's brow furrowed. "Should I?"

Sam shrugged, but the impassivity of his face slipped a little. Josh studied him for a moment.

"You care a great deal about her, don't you?"

"Yes," Sam said flatly, without equivocation. Then he eyed Josh steadily. "But I also know when I'm licked."

He turned on his heel and walked away, leaving Josh pondering his rather cryptic words. Cryptic because the only explanation that made sense out of them seemed impossible.

Chapter 13

There was no answer when Hunter knocked on the door of Josh's house, but when she tried the knob, it swung open. Odd, she thought. But maybe he just feels he doesn't have anything left worth stealing, not with Jason gone. She stepped inside.

The house was quiet, with that deserted feel of emptiness. Her brow furrowed. Josh had said he'd be here, that he'd rather meet her here than at the office. Yet she felt the house was undeniably empty.

"You and your feelings," she muttered under her breath.

She walked into the kitchen, thinking perhaps he'd decided to break down and eat something. It was as empty as the rest of the house. She stood for a moment, puzzled. Then a movement outside caught her eye, and she took a step toward the window.

Her heart twisted in pained sympathy as she watched Josh slice viciously through the water of the pool, swimming at a breakneck pace that had little do with enjoyment, or even exercise, and everything to do with rage and frustration.

When at last he stopped, he took only a minute to catch his breath at the edge of the pool before lifting himself out in one smooth, graceful movement.

Hunter's breath caught in her throat. Color and warmth flooded her face, and she was grateful for the safe concealment of the kitchen curtains.

Safe? She would have laughed if she'd had the breath. Looking at Josh Kincaid's near-naked six foot two, clad only in a pair of wet, blue nylon running shorts, was about as safe as a dropped match in a fireworks factory, and with about the same potential for pyrotechnics.

She watched as he bent to pick up a towel, her eyes traveling over him with an avidity she couldn't seem to help. The journey up the long, muscles lines of his legs to the edge of the blue shorts seemed to take forever, but when she was done, she thought she could have sculpted them in marble. But who would want them in cold, harsh stone when they were so magnificent in warm, living flesh?

When she had reached the point at which the blue fabric clung wetly, lovingly to the tightly muscled swell of his buttocks, she forced her eyes abruptly and swiftly upward, fighting the sudden heat that rose within her. Her fingers curled reflexively, and she denied with every bit of resolution left in her that it was because she wanted to touch that tempting curve.

What she found her eyes on now did nothing to cool that rising heat; in fact, it grew nearly unbearable as her gaze went from the broad, muscled expanse of his chest and the slightest dusting of hair over his breastbone, down to his navel and the feathery trail that thickened slightly as it disappeared below the waist of the shorts.

Involuntarily her fingers tightened further, and her denial that it was because she wanted to run them through that trail of silky hair was a little wobbly. The thought of what she would reach if she followed that inclination sent her already soaring temperature sky-rocketing, and she whirled away from the window.

Almost desperately she ran to the living room, dropping down in one of the chairs before the window with relief; her knees had been shaking. What was happening to her? She had never reacted to a man like this in her life.

Because there's never been a man like this in your life; the little inner voice that had become such a nuisance lately was quick with the answer.

It had been easier, she thought, when he'd been so defenseless, when he'd been nearly buckling under the ugly weight of guilt. She had been able to convince herself then that he just needed her help and that she was naturally responding to that need.

But this Josh, this barely controlled dynamo, this man in whom defenselessness had been replaced with fierce, fighting spirit might need her professional help, but the need he had displayed the other morning had been anything but helpless. And she found herself responding to him even more; more quickly, more completely and, God help her, more hotly.

Never had she had such thoughts about a man that the sight of him in those blue shorts, the wet nylon clinging to every luscious inch, had brought on. It didn't matter that she worked with dozens of equally fit, equally—well, maybe not quite—good-looking men every day. None of them even came close to causing the reaction in her that this man did.

She couldn't even tell herself it was because she'd been living a solitary life since Dan had left her. There had been ample opportunity for her to change that over the years, often with some of those same, fit, good-looking men, but she had never cared enough to or even wanted to. Until now.

She almost laughed at the irony of it, but it became a quivering little shudder instead. You finally find the man who shakes you out of six years of emotional and physical lethargy, and it's under such impossible circumstances that you're fated to failure before you begin, she thought. And that pesky little voice was right there to gleefully point out that Josh Kincaid was obviously not a man to accept the idea of either failure or impossible circumstances.

"Hunter?"

She froze in her chair as his voice came from behind her. Taking in a deep breath, she composed herself, got up and turned to face him.

"Hi."

She managed to get it out before her relief that he had pulled on a pair of jeans was erased by the fact that, except for the towel draped around his neck, he hadn't put on anything else. With his hair wet and slicked back, the firm lines of his jaw and the corded muscles of his neck were solidly male, and the expanse of his chest was—

Was overwhelming, Hunter thought ruefully as he crossed the room to sit in the chair next to hers. She wasn't at all sure her professionalism, shaky at best when he was around, could stand an evening of looking at his bare torso. Lord, how am I supposed to do this, she wondered as she sat back down weakly.

"Is something wrong?" Josh leaned toward her. "Jason?"

"No," she said hastily at the anxiety in his voice. The one chink in his considerable armor, she thought. "I'm sorry. I was... preoccupied."

"I meant to be out front when you got here," he said as he sat back again. "Are the squatters still out there?"

"The reporters? No. Baldwin's keeping to his end of the deal. He hasn't leaked who I am, so the furor seems to be fading naturally."

He sighed glumly. "I don't think I'll ever hold another press conference."

"I swore off even reading newspapers a long time ago."

About six years ago, Josh guessed, when her own tragedy had been front-page news. Although he would never tell her, he had had one of his staff get him copies of the papers that had so avidly followed the story. He had told himself it was so he would know what to expect, know just how far the press would go.

He even believed it, until the moment when he had sat at his desk staring down at the front-page photograph of Hunter, looking frail and fragile in a swath of black, at her tiny son's funeral. The look of utter devastation on her face had torn at him as nothing before in his life had, except for that moment when he'd had to admit he had driven away his own son.

But he had a chance, he thought. As long as he knew Jason had wanted to come home, he knew he hadn't lost him completely. Hunter had never had even that; there had never been a second chance for her.

Yet she hadn't surrendered to despair. She had battled her way out of it, had derived the only possible good out of a mortal blow by dedicating her life to saving others from that hell. The newsprint picture had blurred then, and he'd had to blink rapidly against the sting of tears.

His tears the night he'd read Jason's story had been the first he'd shed in nearly thirty years. Those had been for the pain of his son, and for the mess he'd made of their lives; these were for Hunter's pain, and for the shining beauty she'd made of hers.

It came to him then, as the memory of that heartrending photo formed in his mind, that she had worn an echo of that look the night they had been too late for Jason, as if this had become a calamity as personal to her as her own.

Every case is special to her. He dragged out the old saw again and tried to ignore the fact that it didn't work very well anymore. Before his mind, already out of kilter from Sam's implication, took off on the impossible tangent again, he yanked it back to the matter at hand.

"Sam said I'll have to stall him tomorrow."

She nodded, glad to be back on safe ground. That is, as safe as she could be with that tempting expanse of bare skin to distract her. She took a piece of paper out of the file that was now dog-eared from use and spread it out on the coffee table.

"This is the setup."

Josh bent forward to look at the diagram, carefully hand drawn and labeled.

"This is the courtyard," she said, pointing at the larger wing, "and this is where the phone is."

He saw it labeled in the corner where a shorter wing of the building joined at right angles to the longer one. He nodded.

"The parking area is here." She tapped a spot on the diagram. "You'll have to pull in off of the side street, here." She looked up at him. "I'm sorry you'll have to go alone, but he might be watching the house to make sure you leave alone. And you'd better take the car, not the truck."

He nodded. He was feeling better, he realized, at least as if he was doing something. Or was it just Hunter's presence that had relieved some of the pressure that had been building?

"We'll be around. Discreetly, of course. It's likely he won't call from anywhere close, but we can't take any chances. And we'll be ready to move if he decides to send you somewhere else. We'll loose the trace, but you'll never be out in the open alone."

Josh shrugged; at this point that was the least of his worries. "You think he might drag this out?"

"Maybe. If we are dealing with an amateur here, he's likely to be unpredictable. And we don't want to miss a chance if he makes a stupid mistake. We'll be in place long before six, in case he comes by to check it out beforehand."

She pointed to a spot on the map. "We've got a van already parked out on the street. That's where the receiver is for the bug on the phone and a hookup to a phone-company security for the trace. Got a video camera, too, and one-way glass. All the superspy stuff." She grinned again. "The maintenance guys are going to have a fit. We threw dirt and mud all over the van to make it look like it's been there forever."

God, she made him feel so much better, he thought. Of course, she could also make him furious with those off-the-wall questions of hers, or in those moments when he knew her mind was racing but he couldn't quite follow the intuitive leaps she made. But no one else had been able to bring a ray of light into the darkness of the past week and a half. They *were* doing something, not just spinning their wheels, waiting.

"Where will you be?" He didn't like the idea of her not being there.

"In the van. I'm going tonight, as a matter of fact."

"You're spending the night in that van?" he asked with a frown.

She shrugged. "I'm due there at midnight. We want to be there, in case he *is* watching. And we can check out the buildings so we know they're empty before we start this dance."

"We?"

"The 'bug man' will be there. He's very proprietary about his gadgets," she said lightly. Josh didn't look convinced.

"At least I'll be inside," she said. "It's better than the night I spent in the pouring rain watching an empty warehouse last year."

Last year. Last year he hadn't even known she existed. Hell, last month he hadn't even known she existed. And even if he had, he doubted he would have believed it, that a woman who looked as she did wasn't just another variation of Cynthia.

He would have written her off as just another pretty face, never guessing at what lay beneath the exquisite exterior. He might still have wanted her, responded to her, but only from safely behind his walls. It had taken the horror of Jason's disappearance to batter down some of those walls and make him see her. And it had taken Hunter to make him see that he'd been so busy protecting himself from any more hurt his barriers had effectively closed out the one person he hadn't meant to: Jason.

"Josh?"

He came back to the present abruptly. Great, he thought ruefully. Those people who keep touting my supposed intellect would get a big laugh out of watching me around Hunter Garrett.

"Er...what?"

"Are you all right?"

"Yeah," he muttered. "I was just preoccupied." He realized he had echoed her earlier words and smiled wryly. "Must be the air in here."

She smiled widely, and the air he'd quipped about seemed suddenly in short supply.

"Let's get away from it," he said abruptly, standing up. "And from this damn room." He hated even talking to her in this place that reeked so of Cynthia. He couldn't wait to get outside and walked swiftly toward the back of the house.

After a moment's hesitation, Hunter picked up the sketch and followed, resolutely trying to look at the pool as they walked toward the small gazebo. Formed in the uneven shape of a lagoon, surrounded by plants and a rocky "shoreline," including a lovely waterfall at one end, the pool seemed more like some hidden grotto than the requisite Orange County swimming pool. She tried to concentrate on that and not on the image in her mind of a graceful, muscular male body, sparkling and sleek with water as it rose out of the water. She was grateful when he stopped down on one of the cushioned seats and turned back to business.

"What next?" He sounded a little edgy, as if moving out here hadn't solved the problem.

"The call itself."

He took a breath. "Okay."

"The most important thing is to make sure he knows that nothing, but *nothing* happens until you know Jason is all right. Make him let you talk to him."

The thought of talking to his son made him feel suddenly queasy. "What if he's not with him?"

"Then you demand a second call. Make it clear you don't move an inch without it."

He nodded.

"And you want Jason at the drop. There, visible, so you can see he's all right before you turn over the money. He won't want to go for that, but push it."

Josh swallowed heavily, then nodded again.

"I'd like to say it will be academic," she said, "and that we'll have him back before then, but we have to be prepared."

"I know." He had few illusions left anymore.

"All right. Now, the second thing is the length of the call. That's going to be crucial. You've got to keep him talking long enough for the trace, but we don't know exactly how long that will be."

"Great."

"I know, but there are a million ways to do it. Simple is best. You don't have anything to write on. Your pencil broke. You dropped something. That kind of thing."

He looked startled. "A kidnapper is going to fall for 'Hold on, my pen ran out of ink'?"

"It's so ordinary, it throws them." She quirked an eyebrow at him. "It threw you."

"You," he said dryly, "make a habit of doing that."

She averted her eyes as that sore spot was hit again. She knew what he meant, and she wanted to tell him that she did, that he'd been right about the Garrett mystique. She wanted to apologize for what she'd let happen and how it had affected him. But now was not the time; they had too much to cover. She resolutely went back to business.

"There are other things you can do. You can pretend it's a bad connection, that you can't hear him. Make him repeat things."

He nodded once more, then leaned back on the cushioned seat, one hand fiddling with the end of the towel that still hung around his neck.

Hunter quickly looked at the paper in her hand, as if she were studying the diagram she already knew by heart, since she had drawn it. The sight of muscle rippling under golden skin when he had moved had sent a hot little dart of longing through her that she was afraid would show in her eyes if she didn't look away. She cleared her throat and began again.

"You can quibble about the drop point, the time, anything that will keep him talking."

Josh looked at her uneasily. "What if...I don't want to provoke the guy. Not while he's got Jason."

"I know. If you feel like you're starting to lose him, you'll have to back off." She risked a quick look at him. "You'll be able to tell. You didn't get to where you are without knowing how to negotiate and when you've pushed as far as you can. It won't be easy. You're going to be worried about Jason and angry at this man, but you'll have to hold it all back."

He lifted his gaze to her once more. She was looking at him steadily, with certainty that he could handle this. Her confidence in him warmed him in a way he never would have expected.

"Thank you for not trying to paint a pretty picture for me," he said quietly.

"A week ago I might have. You don't need it now."

She spoke with such calm assurance that, just for a moment, he let himself take it personally. He let himself think that the glow in her eyes and the warmth that seemed to reach out and envelop him were truly meant for him, not just another victim that she was, for the moment, forced to deal with. The strength of his response to that moment of concession to an irresistible urge nearly overwhelmed him, and this time it was he who hastily spoke.

"What if he gets suspicious and just hangs up?"

"He won't, not before he gives you his instructions for the drop. Or at least instructions on when he'll contact you again. But he might throw you a curve or two. You need to be ready for that."

For the next two hours she drilled him, threw hypothetical questions at him, made him run through countless possible variations on how the call might go. She was relentless, pushing, driving, and as he watched her pace the small gazebo as she fired all the possibilities at him, he wondered how someone could look so very delicate yet have such an indefatigable, stubborn strength. He felt on the edge of exhaustion himself.

"You'll do fine," she told him at last. "Just remember you're dealing with the bastard who's keeping Jason from coming home."

The epithet was vehement in the midst of her calm words, and one look at her told him she meant it in the worst possible way. It was getting harder and harder to believe this wasn't personal to her.

"What if the trace works and we still don't know anything?"

She stopped her pacing and stared out at the pool, which was glittering gold in the last rays of the sun. After a long moment she said doggedly, "We keep going."

He got up then, walking over to stand close behind her. "Even if you have to do it on your own time?"

She whirled around, a little gasp escaping her as she came up unexpectedly against his broad, bare chest. Automatically his hands went to her shoulders to steady her. At least, that's what he meant to do, but once he had, he couldn't seem to stop himself from pulling her into his arms.

"Sam told me," he said softly. "He said you fought with your boss over it."

She let out a long, sighing breath, but didn't pull away. "Sam talks too much."

"Why didn't you tell me they were giving you such a hard time?" He gave a harsh chuckle. "Maybe I could have thrown around a little of this clout I supposedly have."

"You have enough to think about without worrying about changing investigators midstream."

His arms tightened around her. "I wouldn't have worried. I would have called our charming Mr. Baldwin. How would your boss have liked it in headlines that he pulled his best investigator off of a front-page case?"

Hunter leaned back in his arms to look up at him. The light of battle was clear in his eyes even in the fading light, and she knew he meant what he'd said. He would have wasted no time in worrying, but would have turned one of the greatest pressures he was enduring to his advantage, using them as they were trying to use him. This, she thought, was how Kincaid Industries had been built; admiration and respect welled up in her. Along with the creeping heat that was spreading through her at the feel of his arms around her, it was a powerful combination that left her trembling in its wake.

Josh felt the little tremor that went through her and lifted one hand to press her head to him. His heart began to hammer at the first touch of the soft skin of her cheek against his naked chest, and his throat tightened at the way she let him hold her there.

"God, Hunter," he whispered, his hand smoothing the silk of her hair, "no one's ever done anything like that for me before. Especially not that way, secretly, without expecting something in return."

She couldn't seem to think of anything except the feel of him, the incredible sensation of having her cheek against that muscled wall.

"I couldn't let him pull me. Not now," she finally managed to say.

"Why?" He hadn't meant to ask it, but it slipped out before he could stop it.

All the reasons leaped to her lips, all the logical, rational explanations of why she had to continue on the case, but somehow she couldn't say any of them. She didn't dare; she was afraid they would all come out the same: because of you.

"Hunter?"

She didn't dare speak, but she could move, and she couldn't resist the urge to slip her arms around his waist. Her hands flexed involuntarily against the smooth skin of his back, her fingers savoring the heat, the hard muscle beneath that skin.

She heard him suck in a gulping breath, then felt the ripple as he swallowed heavily. She felt his arms flex to pull her closer, and she suddenly realized she was doing exactly what she had told herself over and over again she couldn't do—melting at his first touch.

She lifted her head, knowing she had to pull away, had to tell him—

The words died unspoken when her eyes met his. The clear blue had gone dark and smoky, and she could have sworn the floor shifted under her. It must have, or why else would she have swayed forward when she'd meant to pull away?

She felt the heat of him, searing her through the thin cotton of her shirt. She tried to move her arms, to take them from around his waist, but as if they had a will of their own, they slid up the sleek, hot skin of his back.

She smothered an involuntary sound of protest when he loosened his embrace, only to have her breath rush out in a tiny gasp when his hands moved to cup her face and tilt it toward his. Slowly, as if he were fighting the urge, he lowered his head. She knew she had to stop him now, before he stole all her strength away....

But all she could do was look at his mouth, at his parted lips. And then they were on hers, and any protest was beyond her. That hot, sweet fire she'd never felt before him flooded her, radiating out in widening ripples as his mouth coaxed and caressed. Then she felt his tongue, tracing her lips with a feathery lightness, until she could do nothing else but part them for him.

His tongue probed deeply, and she met it eagerly with her own, forgetting entirely that only moments before she had been trying desperately to run from this. She had tried for so long to put the memory away, to convince herself that it hadn't been like this; all her efforts went up in ashes as wave after wave of sensation rippled along nerves she'd thought didn't exist anymore. But they did; they were awake and sizzling, shocked to life by the force that was Josh Kincaid. She would regret it later, she knew, but right now...

Her hands began to move, seemingly of their own volition. His fingers traced the muscles of his back, the back she had longed to touch all evening. They slipped up behind his neck, threading through the thick, dark hair and savoring the heavy silk of it.

Without breaking the kiss, his hands left her face to slide down her back, his fingers splaying out between her shoulders. She felt his arms tighten, crushing her breasts against his chest, and she twisted against him convulsively, helpless against the wave of pleasure that swept through her at the feel of that hot, hard expanse.

She heard an odd little sound, half groan, half growl, rising from deep in his throat. Then his kiss became fierce, demanding, and her bones turned to some hot, flowing liquid as she sagged against him.

She moved her arms, trying to brace herself with her hands. But the solid mass she pressed her palms against for support was his chest, and it seared her with his heat. She spread her fingers wide, unable to stop them from curling, and they brushed over the flat nubs of his nipples. He went suddenly rigid, a smothered, constricted breath escaping him as he broke the kiss.

"God, Hunter," he gasped.

"Yes," she said slowly, dreamily, looking up at him.

"Don't," he groaned.

"Don't what?" Her voice was soft, flowing over him like warm honey.

"Don't look at me like that," he grated.

Her lips, lips that were full and swollen from his kiss, were parted for her quickened breathing. Her eyes were wide, darkened to deepest emerald and shadowed by the thick, dark lashes.

"Oh, hell," he muttered helplessly, and with his hands at her waist, kissed her again. He couldn't resist the temptation of the ripe curves beneath the cotton shirt, and his hands slid up her slender rib cage to cup them tenderly. She moved against him, twisting as if she wanted to press herself into his hands. The movement sent heat ripping through him, and he groaned against her lips.

His fingers crept upwards, searching, and when he found the peaks of her breasts already taut, waiting, he had to tear his mouth away for a gasping breath.

"Hunter," he said thickly, "I—"

He stopped, still breathing raggedly, his hands still cradling her silken curves gently. She twisted again, a tiny, purring sound rising from her as she pressed forward. That small movement, which pushed her taut nipples against his hands like two points of searing fire, sent Josh so close to the edge that he nearly toppled over. He groaned and grasped her arms tightly as he held her away from him, staring down at her. He saw the hot, dazed look start to fade from the green eyes, to be replaced by uncertainty and then the beginnings of retreat.

"Don't," he whispered, harshly, pulling her back into a fierce embrace. "Please, Hunter, don't."

"Josh—"

"I tried," he said raggedly. "I really tried. I told myself a hundred times a day that you were right, that it was just the circumstances. I tried, but you just wouldn't cooperate."

"I wouldn't...?"

"You wouldn't go away. All day long, no matter where I was or what I was doing, there you were. Sneaking into my mind the minute my guard was down. At first it was every time I thought of Jason, and that's damn near twenty-four hours a day."

He gave a short little laugh. "Then you started creeping in on your own, no matter how I tried to stop you. Even when I was furious with you, or with myself for letting you get to me, you were there."

"I—"

He put a finger to her lips. "And the nights? Oh, let me tell you about those." He laughed harshly this time. "I've had dreams like I haven't had since I was fourteen. It's gotten so I hate being awake to think about Jason, and I'm afraid to go to sleep, because there you'll be."

Hunter stared up at him, wide-eyed. "But...you haven't...since that morning...I thought you were sorry."

He knew she meant the morning in the parking lot, the morning that seemed an eon ago now.

"No, I haven't," he said through gritted teeth. Hunter drew back at his fierceness, more confused than ever. "I wasn't sorry, lady, I was scared."

"Scared...?" She sounded doubtful.

"You still don't get it, do you?" he muttered incredulously. Suddenly, almost violently he pulled her against him, his hands slipping down to her hips to press them tightly against his.

"That's why," he hissed, knowing she couldn't help but feel his full, hard arousal. "That's what just looking at you does to me, like some half-grown kid with his hormones on a rampage. And not my mind, my common sense, my will, not even Jason can stop it. And believe me, I've tried them all."

Hunter just stared at him, lips parted as she struggled for breath. She couldn't seem to get enough air, whether it was because of the shock of his words or the feel of that rigid column of flesh pressing against her, she didn't know. She only knew that the pool below them should be boiling from their reflected heat.

She tried desperately to summon up the discipline that had served her so well since the death of her son, tried to put some distance between them. For the first time, it failed her. He had had the courage to name what was between them, to quit pretending it didn't exist; in the lingering heat of his touch, she told herself she could do no less.

"Oh, Josh," she breathed, "so have I."

He froze, forgetting to breathe as he stared hotly down at her, trying to suppress the shudder that rippled through him at the feel of her soft warmth pressing against his hardened flesh.

"You...have?"

"I've tried so hard to tell myself it's wrong. That I couldn't let it become...personal. I'm a professional, and you're..." She faltered.

"I'm what?" he asked, a little shakily.

"You're the man who made me want to throw away all the rules," she whispered. "The one who made me spitting mad one minute and ready to hug him the next." His eyes widened at that, but she kept on. "You're the one who made me feel...things I never thought I'd feel again, things I've never felt at all. And scared me to death because of them."

Deep down inside her somewhere, she knew she might regret this, but she couldn't seem to care. All the feelings she'd been repressing about this man, the man who'd had the strength and force and drive to overcome a childhood that would have destroyed many, yet still had enough compassion to try and help the angry, rebellious and frightened teenager who had put him through hell, welled up inside her, and she couldn't fight them anymore.

"Hunter?" His voice was low and thick; he was afraid to believe what he was hearing.

"Yes," she said softly, for the first time making no effort to hide the desire swirling up inside her.

He saw it in her eyes, and it hit him so hard it took his breath away. Her quiet answer echoed in his ears, and in less time than it took for him to be certain he'd heard her right, his body surged to full response.

He pulled her hard against him. This time the kiss was mutual, hungry with rising need and want. It was a match held to two fires that had been banked and held back for far too long, and any doubt or hesitation was singed to ash in the resulting flare of heat.

Chapter 14

Josh couldn't get enough. He'd waited so long, he wanted to devour her, and he stroked every surface, every hidden, sensitive place in her honeyed mouth with his tongue. He felt her hands slip around his neck, felt her fingers tangle in his hair, and a shudder went through him. She made a small, soft sound that was like a feather running up his spine, and then her tongue met his, danced over it lightly before pushing forward to run over the ridge of his teeth. That feather became a searing ripple of fire.

Hunter couldn't believe what was happening to her. She clung to him as he gently lowered her to the floor of the gazebo, tugging the pads from the seat to cushion her. It wouldn't have mattered; all she knew was heat, glowing, melting heat, flowing through her from every place he touched.

And as he touched her, she was suddenly consumed with the need to touch him, to feel the golden skin again, to trace the long, lean lines that were etched so clearly in her mind. She slid eager fingers over his back, the searing heat of his sleek skin sending flickers of sensation along every nerve. With a low sigh of satisfaction, her searching hands slipped around him, moving to stroke the muscled smoothness of his chest.

He'd been on fire from her kiss, and the sounds she'd made had added fuel to the flame; her hands on his bare skin turned that flame into an inferno. He couldn't be any hotter, he thought, then her exploring fingers found the flat nubs of his nipples again, and white-hot heat turned the thought to cinders. He closed his eyes, a low groan escaping him as he lifted himself away.

"Josh?" It was barely a whisper. "What's wrong?"

His voice came out as a hoarse, unintelligible sound, and he had to wait and try again.

"I should take you inside," he finally managed. "But I don't want to. Not there. Not in her house."

Hunter's heart suddenly took off and soared; she understood everything those whispered words implied, perhaps even better than he did. She looked up at him, lifting a finger to trace the rugged line of his jaw.

"I...like this place," she said huskily.

The unexpected touch of shyness in her eyes and voice turned his already churning insides to some melting, flowing liquid that seemed to drain him of the strength to do anything but just look at her.

The thickly fringed green eyes were wide and dark, fastened on him with a look that matched what he was feeling. Her lips were parted, looking full and thoroughly kissed, and her breath was coming in short little gasps that made her breasts rise and fall with quick regularity beneath the green cotton shirt.

"God, you're beautiful."

She looked startled, then lowered her eyes in embarrassed pleasure. He stared for a moment at the lowered semicircles of her lashes, dark and thick against flushed cheeks, then bent his head to press his lips against her hair. He tried to smother the words that rose in him, damned the innate sense of honor that forced him to say them.

"If you're not sure, Hunter, tell me now," he said hoarsely. "I don't think I'll be able to stop again."

She lifted her head to look at him, this man who had blown away all her defenses, who had battered them down with the mere fact of his being. In a world where she all too often saw people at their worst, she had lost hope that anyone like him existed.

She gave him her answer. She kissed him as if she'd hungered for him for years, as if she'd saved all the yearnings, longings and needs of those years to pour into this one kiss.

Josh was reeling; he'd never been kissed like this in his life, never imagined a kiss like this. Kisses were a prelude, or in Cynthia's case a commodity, most often in short supply. They were a mildly pleasurable practice, not a cataclysm that shook his very foundations, that disrupted every nerve, shattered any semblance of sanity.

He clenched his jaw, trying to regain control, but when he saw the little shivers that were rippling through her slender body, he knew it was all right; he wasn't alone—she was right there with him, and it was all right. If he'd had any doubts left, they had been seared away by the racing wildfire of that kiss; she wanted him, and the knowledge was gunpowder to the open flame.

He trailed hot, sweet kisses over her, from the delicate arch of her brow to the pert tip of her nose, over the soft fullness of her mouth to the feisty chin, down the fine line of her jaw to her throat. He pressed his mouth, hungry and eager, down the delicate curve of her neck, pausing at the hollow of her throat to relish the silken feel of her skin and revel in the rapid pounding of her pulse beneath his lips.

All the while his hands were moving, stroking every curve, until Hunter was a mass of aching need to feel his hands on her bare skin. When at last his hand slid up beneath her shirt, she gasped at the heat of it. She moaned aloud at the first touch of his fingers on the heated flesh of her breast. As his lips nibbled along her collarbone, his fingers crept up to stroke her nipple through the silky fabric of her bra; it tightened instantly to his touch, sending a jolt through her that was matched by the one racing up his arm from fingers that couldn't quite believe the intensity of her response to him.

She'd never felt like this, never been so inundated with so many sensations at once. She wanted to be rid of the last barriers between them, she wanted his mouth on her naked flesh; she wanted hers on his; she wanted to give herself to him in ways she'd never even thought of—her own eagerness shocked her and thrilled her at the same time.

He tugged her shirt free of her jeans and pushed it gently upward. He released the clasp of her bra and freed her from the tangle of pale green cotton and nylon, and Hunter gave a little gasp of shocked pleasure at the feel of the cool evening air on her nakedness. Then his mouth was on her, tracing the curves of her breasts with his tongue, and her gasp became a cry of need.

He teased her swelling flesh relentlessly, his hand at one breast, his mouth on the other. When at last he reached that aching little peak with his lips, she gasped again at the shock that ripped through her as her nipples rose to his tongue.

"Oh, God, Josh," she gasped. "I want..."

"What?" he murmured thickly, lifting his head from her breast. "Tell me, Hunter, tell me what you want."

"Everything," she moaned, reaching to pull his head back down to the hard, puckered flesh that was so cold and bereft without the wet heat of his mouth.

"God, Hunter," he groaned against her breast, "so do I. I want everything with you. I want to see you, touch you, and want to feel your hands on me everywhere...."

With a sudden convulsive movement, he reached for the snap at the waist of her jeans, those damn tight jeans that so tantalized him. He halted for an instant, looking at her. With a breathy little sigh, she shifted her body to make it easier for him, and he tugged them off. He caught a glimpse of pale green panties that matched the bra, but they slid down her slender legs with the denim and were forgotten.

"Oh, Hunter," he said softly, closing his eyes for a moment, as if he couldn't bear it all at once. He reached for her, wanting to touch, to know every silken inch of her, wanting to feel the silken weight of her full breasts in his hands, wanting to—

"You, too. Please?"

It was a low, husky plea, and it turned him inside out. He kicked out of his jeans and briefs, noticing inanely that they were as warm from his overheated body as if they'd come out of a dryer. He turned back to her, feeling a little self-conscious at the way those green eyes were drinking him in—he felt like... Like she must feel when you look at her, that little voice inside him answered.

It was the strangest feeling he'd ever had. Cynthia had made him feel like a lusting piece of meat; most of the others he'd ever been with had made him feel like he was in some kind of unknown competition, with them as the judges, using a scoring system he'd never known about. When Hunter looked at him like that, it made him feel humble and proud at the same time.

"I was right," she murmured as she looked at him in the last, fading rays of the California sun, "marble wouldn't do you justice."

He had no idea what she meant, but the look in her eyes told him he shouldn't worry about it. With a soft little sigh, she lay back, bending one leg at the knee, and he saw her fingers curl around the edge of the cushion beneath her. The thought of them curling like that around something else sent an explosive burst of swirling heat to that rigid core of him, and with a low groan he pulled her to him once more.

Hunter couldn't be still; she wanted to touch, to feel, to taste, to do everything her fevered body demanded. When his lips claimed her breast again, she wanted to cry out her pleasure, and when his fingers claimed her other nipple at the same time, she did cry out. It fired his blood, and he switched places, his fingers moving to tease the taut crest still wet from his mouth, while his lips and tongue flicked the other peak to pebble-hard tightness.

Involuntarily she arched her back, thrusting her breasts up to him, wanting more even though it was already making her mindless. He moved over her, burying his face between the firm curves, kissing wherever he touched, loving the feel of her as she pressed him close. His hand slid down over her flat belly, stroking, caressing, at last parting the soft, reddish curls below.

He felt her tense and paused, pressing soft kisses down her body, circling her navel with his tongue and returning to her throbbing breasts.

"Hunter?" he asked softly.

"I...it's been a long time."

"You think I don't know that?" He lifted his head and forced her to meet his eyes. "You don't have to tell me there haven't been many since your husband," he began, then he saw the flicker come and go in her eyes. "There hasn't been anyone, has there."

His quiet words weren't a question, but she shook her head, a short, quick movement that spoke worlds about her self-consciousness.

"Oh, Hunter—" he hugged her tightly "—do you have any idea what that means to me? That after all this time..."

He faltered, knowing he couldn't find the words right now to tell her what it meant to him that she had chosen him.

"I won't hurt you. I promise," he said against the silk of her hair.

Despite the urgent, demanding size and heat of him she could feel pressed against her, she believed him. And suddenly the thought of the pulsing part of him moving inside her left her gasping in anticipation. Hungrily, eagerly, she pressed her lips to his chest, loving the taste of him, the hot sleekness of him.

She let her tongue slip between her lips to tease his flesh, and felt the ripple of muscle in his belly as he sucked in a deep breath. She moved in widening circles, leaving sizzling paths across his skin that he swore would be scars by tomorrow. When the tip of her hot, wet, probing tongue flickered over his nipples, he made a choking sound and in one swift, frenzied movement, pressed her back against the cushions.

This time she made no protest as he explored her body, and when his fingers began to probe ever so gently between her thighs, she parted them for him without hesitation. He smothered a groan when he found her slick and ready.

Control, Kincaid, he muttered to himself. Cynthia taught you all about control. You're famous for it, remember? Even making love, he'd been told that—always in control. There was only one problem; if what he'd had with women up to now was making love, then what the hell was this? He didn't know, only knew that he'd never felt it until Hunter, and it was about to tear him apart.

Gritting his teeth, he began a slow, circular stroking, massaging that tender spot he'd found until she was moaning, her hips beginning to move in the same rhythm. He was so intent on his effort at restraint that he was only slightly aware of the soft touch of her hand as it slid down his chest.

The awareness grew with scorching suddenness when he felt slender fingers tangling in the hair that drew downward from his navel. Oh, Lord, he muttered to himself, she touches me and I'm done for. He was about to reach for her hand to move it somewhere, anywhere, else, when he heard her softly whispered words.

"I've wanted to do this for so long...."

He froze. "What?"

"Touch you like this. Ever since that morning you were in the kitchen with your shirt open..."

She trailed off shyly, and he felt a little shock of wonder. He hadn't been out in left field all this time.

"Why didn't you say—?"

He broke off abruptly; her hand had resumed its explorations. He lost track of all rational thought as his earlier fantasy suddenly came true and Hunter's fingers found and curled around him. He gasped, throwing his head back, every muscle in his body tensing.

"God, Hunter!"

The words burst from him as he tried to pull away, but instead found himself pushing harder against her hand. She stroked him, hesitantly at first but then with more assurance as tremor after tremor swept through him.

Revelations were sweeping through Hunter nearly as fast. First at the sleek, satin weight of him in her hand, then at the odd feeling of feminine power that filled her at his quivering response. She marveled at it even as she realized her own body was rapidly careening out of control.

"Hunter, stop," he ground out, sweat beading his forehead. "It's been too long, and I want you too much...."

"Then stop waiting," she whispered.

She looked up at him as he moved over her, aware by the veins pulsing along every strained, taut muscle the effort he was putting into moving slowly. She lifted her hands to run them down the long muscles of his arms, trembling now from the exertion, then she felt him, hot and hard and probing.

She sucked in a breath at the feel of it when he first began to sink into her. God, he was stretching her, filling her so full! Then he stopped, looking down at her with a question in those incredible eyes, and she knew if she didn't have all of him now she would die.

With sudden urgency she reached out, sliding her hands from his arms down his sides to grasp his lean hips and pull him forward. He resisted for a brief second, afraid of hurting her, but when her hands moved to cup the taut curve of his buttocks, urging him on, he gasped in shocked pleasure and thrust forward.

Hunter cried out his name at the exquisite completeness of it. She hadn't known, hadn't realized that part of her had been missing, she knew it now because she was whole again. She lost all desire for gentleness; she wanted him, all of him, driving into her, now, and she lifted her hips invitingly and heard him groan in response.

"Hunter, slow down," he gasped, "I can't—"

"No," she whispered fervently, raising her hips sharply again, forcing him deep inside her. She felt the moment when he gave it up, when he surrendered to the clamorous need and began the driving rhythm that his body had been demanding all along. Hunter's head thrashed on the mat. She knew the small, animal sounds that rose at his every thrust were coming from her; she didn't, couldn't, care.

Josh could only hope he wasn't hurting her; he was beyond stopping. His vaunted reputation for control was in fragments now, had been ever since Hunter had turned into a writhing, passionate spitfire beneath him. He felt her hands clutching him, nails digging into his back and buttocks, heard her cries as he moved within her, each sound firing him to a new urgency until he thought the heat would simply turn him to ashes right here.

He'd wanted to be gentle; he'd seen the look in her eyes when he'd first slipped into her caressing heat. She was so incredibly tight he'd wondered if he'd last long enough to be gentle, and the sheer heat of her had nearly melted his determination right then. But still he'd tried, biting back the cries that rose to his lips at her every sign that she wanted more.

But then she'd made it crystal clear that all promises were off, and when she began to arch beneath him, driving him into the very depths of her, he'd lost the battle he'd had little hope of winning in the first place.

She was hanging on to him desperately now, her legs locked around his lean waist as he thrust again and again; she was whirling off in some strange, new place full of fire and heat and brilliant light, and he was her only hold on life.

"Josh!" She cried it out on a gasping breath, a touch of alarm in her voice.

"I've got you," came his voice from out of the fiery mist. "Hold on, Hunter, and let it go."

It was absurd advice, but it made perfect sense to her, at least as much sense as she needed here on the edge of...wherever she was. Then it didn't matter, because she wasn't there anymore, she was flying, soaring, exploding into a thousand rainbow pieces, aware only of the pulsing strength of Josh's body inside her, the only assurance she needed that she would come back together again.

Josh was stunned into stillness at the first rippling convulsion of her body. God, he could feel her, tightening, clenching....

It was his last rational thought, for that very sensation he was marveling at pulled him up with her, and his world exploded into a flare of light and heat and throbbing, pulsing pleasure.

He cried out, a guttural, harsh shout of her name that he couldn't hold back as it kept on, in wave after wave of shuddering sensation, until he thought he'd poured his entire soul into her. It didn't matter; he knew there was no safer place for it, and he collapsed atop her, numbed, drained and spent.

His awareness returned in stages, first of the little echoes of that incredible eruption that were still tingling along his singed nerves, then of his own gasping for breath, then eventually of the fact that he was pressing down on Hunter with his full weight. He knew he should move, but he wasn't at all sure he could.

When at last he tried to at least slide sideways off her, she made a little sound of protest and locked her legs around him, holding his body over and inside her. He raised his head to look at her, a lingering wonder blending with the question in his eyes. She wanted him to stay?

"Don't leave me," she whispered, and the touch of wonder that was in his eyes was echoed in her voice. "You feel wonderful right where you are."

He had to close his eyes and turn his head away from her, so strong was the wave of emotion that swept him. Cynthia could never wait to be rid of him, his weight, his body, his entire presence.

"God, Hunter, I..." He trailed off. How could he talk about what had happened between them without sounding like a bad movie? He lifted himself up on his elbows to look at her; she lowered her eyes.

"I've never...been like that," she whispered, her voice tight.

He gave a short, sharp laugh. "Do you think I have?" He lifted her chin with a gentle finger. "I've always been...Mr. Control. I learned it early on from my old man, and just in case I forgot, my dear wife pounded it home again. Even in bed, I never, ever lost control. Until you."

She took a deep breath, and ever so slowly the dark lashes lifted. He ran his thumb caressingly over his lips.

"I don't know how or why," he said softly, "but it's never been like this for me, either. I thought...losing control would be like giving up something, surrendering part of myself. And it is, but..."

"But what?" she whispered, meeting his eyes now.

"I found out," he said hoarsely, "that what I gave up was nothing compared to what I got back."

She hugged him suddenly, fiercely. They lay in silence, the only movement coming when Josh shifted his weight to the side, keeping his leg thrown over hers, and then the slight breeze flitted over their bodies, cooling them and lifting strands of their hair. And at last, there in the gazebo where they had spent that first night in each other's arms, they slept.

It wasn't until the chill overcame even the tremendous heat of Josh's body that Hunter awoke, shivering a little. Sleepily she snuggled closer, and his arms tightened around her. Something was nagging at the edges of her mind, a sleep-drugged mind that had gone for too long without that necessity. She tried to push it away, but it wouldn't go. She opened her eyes.

Reality plunged home with the deadly swiftness of a knife. She sat up abruptly, staring in shock. She was naked, on the floor of the open gazebo with an equally naked Josh, who was stirring even as she looked at him. Her cheeks heated as her eyes stayed along the length of him, and sweet, hot memories formed in her mind with vivid clarity.

His eyes fluttered open then, and when he saw her awake, he yawned and propped himself up on one elbow. He looked so sleepily sexy, with his hair tousled and mussed from her fingers and his jaw shadowed by his beard, she nearly reached for him. Then she saw his eyes slide down to her naked breasts, saw his lips part and felt her nipples begin to tighten in response.

My God, she thought, all it takes is a look....

Hastily she spoke. "Uh...what time is it?"

It took him a moment to tear his eyes from that ripe fullness and comprehend her question. He glanced at his wrist, only to find it as bare as the rest of him. One corner of his mouth twisted sheepishly, then he began to dig in the tangle of their clothes for his watch.

"Nearly one."

Hunter paled. "Damn," she said softly, grabbing for her jeans. "I was supposed to be at the van an hour ago."

Josh sat up. He was awake now, and reality was beginning to return, pushing aside the sweet fantasies of the night.

"Will it make that much difference?"

"To me." Her cheeks were flaming as she pulled on the lacy panties he'd swept off her so easily. It suddenly seemed wrong, being here with him like this, dressing in front of him, after having slept naked in his arms, outside, where anyone could have come across them. "I've never been late before."

"You're not that late now." Some of her tension communicated itself to him, and he began to feel a little uneasy.

"Late enough." She grimaced as she wriggled into her jeans. "I'm lucky they didn't send somebody to look for me." She went from pale to ashen. "Oh, Lord, maybe they did."

She glanced at the house, and Josh knew she was thinking of her car sitting in front. How far would they have come, looking for her? he wondered. The door had been unlocked.... Would they have come out here? Could they have? Lord knows, he wouldn't have noticed. He glanced at her face and saw the same thought in her eyes, even in the shadowy darkness.

"Hunter—"

"No." She shook her head fiercely as she tried to fasten the clasp of her bra with trembling fingers. "I should have known better. I did know better. Talk about violating every rule of ethics."

He stiffened. He knew she was upset, but still the words stung. She stopped her futile efforts then, and looked at him.

"I'm sorry, Josh. I didn't mean that. I wouldn't...trade what happened between us for anything."

"But?" He knew it was coming, and it chilled him.

"I can't handle both," she whispered. "I have to be thinking of Jason, full-time. We both do."

The cold, unalterable truth hit him like a fist in the gut. She was right. They'd stolen these hours, these moments of peace. Jason was in trouble, out there somewhere being held captive, scared and wanting to come home, while his father was at home, keeping the one person who could find him from doing her job.

And, he thought with a sudden flash of heat, experiencing the most incredible pleasure he'd ever felt in his life. Pleasure he had no right to. The chill of guilt overcame the heat of his memories. With hands that were remarkably steady, he reached out and fastened the clasp she'd been fumbling with. Only when his fingers brushed the silken flesh of her breasts did that steadiness waver, and he curled his fingers into fists to hide the tremor.

"You're right," he said after a minute, his jaw clenched tight. He turned away from her then, getting to his feet and reaching for his jeans. Hunter concentrated on pulling on and tucking in her shirt, trying not to notice the flexing of hard, taut muscles in his legs and buttocks as he tugged them on, trying not to remember how they had felt beneath her hands.

They exchanged no words as they walked through the house and out to her car. She froze, unable to move when she saw the small, white card under the wiper. At last Josh reached around her to pull it free.

It was a business card from Sam Singer, with a few hastily scrawled lines on the back. "H—I told them you got a late start on the run-through. They'll wait. Be careful, partner. Sam."

"It's all right," Josh said as he held the card out to her.

She read it quickly. "I owe you one, my friend," she whispered to the absent man who had covered for her, something she'd never needed before in her life.

"Be careful of what?" Josh asked softly.

Hunter looked up at him, and he read the answer in her eyes. Long after she had driven away, he stood in the dark staring after her.

Chapter 15

"I'm sorry, Mr. Kincaid."

Josh looked up at Sam and shrugged. "I expected it."

"You did great, though. Held him more than long enough. That bit about asking directions was great."

"It seemed too easy," Josh said, not sure why it bothered him.

"That's what bothers me."

They were the first words Hunter had spoken since they'd got the depressing news that, while Josh had indeed managed to keep the caller on the line long enough for a trace, it had led them only to a busy convenience store with a bank of pay phones in front. The phone in the center had the number the phone company had told them the call had originated from.

They sat in the undercover van in the market parking lot, watching. There was no sign of anything unusual, just ordinary pedestrian traffic. A lot of it. Hunter guessed glumly that that phone had probably been used at least three times since the call had been made.

"No point in CSI," Sam said, echoing her thoughts.

"No." She sighed. "He's long gone. Let's get started."

Sam nodded, then turned to the driver of the van and his partner, who was the "bug man" who had monitored the phone call. "Don, start with the clerk inside, will you? Marty, try the attendant at the gas station next door. I'll hit the hamburger stand."

The men nodded and piled out of the front seats. Sam paused in the sliding doorway of the van, his eyes flicking from Josh to Hunter. There was understanding in his glance, but no censure. He seemed to think better of whatever he'd been about to say, and left without a word.

Hunter was staring at the notes she had taken while listening to the call, trying not to concede the knowledge she had seen in Sam's eyes. She could feel Josh's eyes on her, knew he must have seen what she'd seen. She tried again to read the notes.

He'd done so well, she thought. He'd used the tricks she'd taught him easily, stalling without giving the least impression that that was what he was doing. He'd even come up with a few of his own, including managing to convince the caller he didn't know the way to the drop point.

"He bought it so easily," she murmured, not even realizing she was saying it aloud.

"I know."

She looked up at him. "You're quite a negotiator, Mr. Kincaid. And that was a neat trick, making him give directions like that."

"You said simple was best. But I still expected it to be harder."

"Me, too." She glanced at her notes, then back at him. "How do you feel about it? Other than it was too easy."

He shrugged. "He seemed...intimidated. And at first it seemed like he was reading it. His voice changed when I threw him one of your curves."

She nodded. "I heard it, too."

The rest of the call had been straightforward, although the caller had seemed very nervous. He had hedged about letting him talk to his son, but Josh had been flintily unmovable. Hunter had been sitting in the van, listening and silently cheering Josh on, full of an unexpected sense of pride at how well he was handling it. At the moment when she was mentally urging him to threaten to hang up, she had heard him saying just that.

"Until I talk to my son, we have nothing more to say. Goodbye."

His voice had been ice, and the caller had buckled as Hunter had let out a soft "Way to go."

From then on, the call had gone Josh's way, as if by the one move he had gained the upper hand. He would call, with Jason, tonight. The drop was in the park that Hunter had selected, and not the crowded playground next to it. It was in daylight, not at night, as the caller had wanted. And most of all, he had agreed that Jason would be there, in sight but not accessible, when the drop was made. It was a triumph, even though the man had insisted he would have a gun on the boy every minute and wouldn't release him until the money had been turned over.

"I'd hate to go up against you in a bargaining session," Sam had quipped when they had all listened to the recording after the call had ended. As soon as they had been certain the call hadn't been from nearby, they had all met beside the van.

"Now what?" Josh asked softly.

She sighed. "Now we hope somebody saw him use the phone. And we hope that of all the people who did, we can figure out which one was him. And we hope that something comes back from those lab tests on the beer and the chili can." She looked at him. "And you wait for a phone call."

"If we can trace just one—"

"Unlikely. He'll guess we'll be trying, since we'll know Jason is with him. The tap is still on your phone, so we'll try, but don't count on anything. The call will probably be too short."

"Damn it," Josh swore softly. "I feel so helpless."

"Don't. You did an incredible job. You ran the whole call."

"Why doesn't that make me feel better?"

"Because he's too nervous. Nervous people are scared people, and scared people do stupid things. Let's just hope we catch him at one."

"That's a lot of hoping."

"Sometimes that's all you have. But sometimes it's enough."

Hunter sat at the desk, rubbing her eyes wearily. She opened them again and peered blearily at the new stack of papers on the desk. Their rounds of the area surrounding the phone booth had been fruitful. Too fruitful. She had more to sort through now than she had before.

She glanced at her watch as she reached for a stack of the cards filled out by Don and Marty in their canvas of the neighborhood. Noon. Twelve hours ago she had been in Josh's arms.

She bit her lip, trying to keep her mind off the sweet, honeyed memories of the night. She had never known she could feel like that, that she even had the capacity to feel like that. Even now, she could almost feel his hands on her, his mouth on her, his body inside hers. A warm heaviness began to pool deep and low inside her, and her breath began to quicken.

She caught herself with a little gasp. Stop it, she ordered herself fiercely.

She stared down at the chaos on the desk and came to a sudden decision. She turned to the computer terminal that sat on the table behind the desk.

Hours later she had the sorts she'd been after; by vehicle, by person interviewed, by time and by place. And she still couldn't find a pattern.

She knew she needed rest, but was afraid to let down her guard, afraid of what lay behind the floodgates of sleep. She glanced at her watch, a little surprised to find it was well after four. She had cut loose the other detectives as soon as they had interviewed everyone in the vicinity of the pay phone, saying she would handle the rest, not out of generosity so much as wanting the work to keep her occupied. And to keep Josh Kincaid out of her mind. It hadn't worked.

She wondered what he was thinking. She knew she had hit him pretty hard, although making him feel guilty over what they had shared hadn't been her intent. She just knew she couldn't afford the distraction right now. The decision hadn't done her much good; she'd been in a state of total abstraction all day.

She propped her elbows on the desk and cradled her head wearily in her hands. When she felt her eyes begin to drift closed, she jerked upright abruptly. The short, sweet moments of sleep in his arms had been all she'd had in days, and it was catching up with her. Beating back the wave of exhaustion that threatened to engulf her, she turned back to the profusion of material on the desk.

The jangling of the phone startled her almost as much as the angle of the sunlight coming in through the window. A quick glance at her watch told her what she'd already guessed by the stiffness of her neck and shoulders; she'd spent over two hours hunched over the mass of data. She grabbed for the receiver.

"Investigator Garrett."

"He called. You were right. It was too short."

"Josh. I'm sorry. Did you talk to Jason?"

"Yes." There was a short pause, and she could almost see his jaw tighten. "He said he was scared. And he wanted to come home. And that—" She heard his sharp intake of breath before he steadied himself and went on. "He said he was sorry he was so much trouble."

Hunter's heart twisted in her chest. "Oh, Josh..."

"Don't. I can't...Just don't."

She drew in a deep breath. "Was that all?"

"Yes. He took the phone away and hung it up."

"Did he ever say anything?"

"No. It was just Jason." She heard something in the background, then he was back. "Sam wants to talk to you." She heard him hand over the phone.

"Hi, Hunter."

"Anything?"

"No. Background was clear as bell. No noise, nothing."

"But not a phone booth?"

"No. Too quiet, no cars, no outdoor noise at all."

She sighed. "All right."

"Want me to stick around here?"

"No. Thanks, Sam. But leave the tape on, just in case."

"Right." Sam hesitated. "Uh, do you want to...uh..."

"Yes. Put him on."

"Okay. I'll be on my way there."

She heard a rustling, some muffled words and then far in the background a door closing.

"You didn't have to send Sam, you know." His voice was flat, inflectionless.

"What?"

It was a second before he said, a little harshly, "It's not like you to dodge a question, Investigator Garrett."

She felt herself flush; he'd seen right through her. She'd sent Sam to monitor the call on purpose, to avoid going herself, and it was obvious Josh knew it. "Josh, I—"

"I am capable of...keeping my hands to myself."

"Perhaps I wasn't worried about you."

He let out a short, sharp breath. "Damn."

"Josh—"

"I know! I know," he repeated, less violently. "Just forget it."

Forget it? Not likely. If she lived a hundred years, she would never forget what he did to her, what he could still do to her. She couldn't, just couldn't, let it happen, not now, not when she needed every bit of her energy just to keep going. She squared her shoulders.

"Is the money ready, in case we have to go through with the drop?"

"Yes."

"The lab is working on the briefcase now. It should be ready in a couple of hours."

"Ready?"

"With a tracking device transmitter. Once we have Jason safe, we can go after whoever picks it up."

"I don't care about it. Not if Jason's all right."

"I know. But I want this guy. I've spent too much time on him to just let him walk. He's put you, and Jason, through too much."

"If I get Jason back, it doesn't matter. He can have the damn money."

"I hope we won't have to—"

"I'm tired of hearing about hope," he said a little sharply.

"I'm tired of talking about it," she returned shortly. "I'm tired of sifting through tons of useless information, talking to people who can't remember what they saw five seconds ago, let alone five minutes, and above all I'm tired of sitting around waiting for a lucky break!"

The pencil she was holding snapped in her hand, and she jumped at the noise. She tossed the pieces down in a disgust aimed more at herself than at the innocent pieces of wood.

"Feel better?" he asked rather acidly.

"No. Do you?"

"No."

"I'll bring you the briefcase. Where?"

"The office. I'm going there now. I can't stand to just sit around here any longer."

"All right."

Josh hung up when he found himself holding the phone, listening to a dial tone. He was beginning to hate the thing. It put too much distance between you. First Jason, then Hunter. God, Jason had sounded so scared, near tears. If that bastard hurt him, he'd track him to the ends of the earth.

Then why had he practically jumped down Hunter's throat when she had said the same thing? He ran a hand wearily through his hair. He didn't know. He only knew he'd been numb since she'd left. His mind was tired, battered from being constantly yanked away from the thoughts of Jason in trouble and the hot, tempting lure of the memories of Hunter in his arms. Even now his body responded to the visions in his mind, and he swore softly. Then loudly. He turned angrily on his heel and headed toward the stairs and a shower. A cold one, he thought sourly. Again.

Hunter tossed the computer readout on the desk with all the other paperwork and stared at the shadows that were beginning to lengthen as the sun crept lower in the west-facing windows of the office. She wondered idly if Victor Curtis was ever coming back to reclaim his desk, or if he would just stay away until he found out she was gone. Suits me, she thought.

She tried to reach for the printout again but couldn't seem to make her hand move. She barely needed it, anyway; she practically had everything on it memorized, for all the good it did her. She couldn't get rid of the feeling that something was sitting in that mass of information, somewhere between the list of every car that had been seen near the phone, the bits and pieces they'd got from neighbors near Rob's house and the growing case file that she carried with her everywhere in case something occurred to her. Something she was just as sure was there as she was sure she wasn't going to find it. She'd been looking at the stuff so long it could be right in front of her and she'd miss it.

I wonder how many pieces there are here, she thought. I should count them. Oh, Lord, I'm really losing it now, she thought. She shook her head against the eerie ringing in her ears, which told her she was reaching the limit of her endurance. She tried to ignore it.

"Hunter?"

She looked up. "Hi, Sam."

"I've got the reports back from the lab."

She didn't have to ask; his face told her. "Nothing," she said dully. "I should have expected as much."

Sam came in and laid the lab reports on top of all the rest. "No match on the one clear print they got. Whoever it is doesn't have a record, or even an application on file with prints." He looked at her for a moment, concern in his eyes. "We did get one little piece of luck. The saliva residue gave us a blood type."

"Let me guess," she said bitterly. "O positive, right?"

"No. That's the lucky part. Type B."

One eyebrow went up, but it came down quickly. "Won't do us much good until we find him." She laughed harshly. "Of course, we could always order tests of everybody who's ever met Jason. Or Josh. Or worked for him. Or heard of him."

Sam's look of concern deepened. "At least we know for sure there *was* somebody else, right? Jason's O positive, and Rob is, too."

"Yeah. Great."

"Hunter, you'd better get some rest. You look," he said frankly, "like hell."

"Thank you, old friend."

"I am. That's why I said it."

Her harsh gaze softened a little. "I know, Sam."

"So give it a rest. You'll need it tomorrow."

She let out a long, tired breath. "I will. I'm going to deliver that—" she gestured at the briefcase sitting on the floor beside the desk "—and then I'm going to go home. Really home. If," she amended wryly, "it's still there."

"Good. The crew is all ready—they'll meet us with the van and the chase cars at six. That'll give us time to scope out the area before the drop at ten."

She nodded wearily, forcing herself to listen as Sam went over the last of the details. When he'd gone to get some rest himself before the drop tomorrow, the thought of home began to appeal more and more to Hunter. She'd almost forgotten what it was like to be in her own home, with her own things around her, not living out of a locker and using a community bathroom. Yes, she would go home, sleep in her own bed and hope that being in the one place that had no connection with Josh would help her keep him out of her mind.

Jason will be home tomorrow, she kept telling herself as she drove to the Kincaid building. Josh had talked to him, he was alive and they would get him back tomorrow. Then she could go after the kidnapper with her full concentration, without the distraction of worrying so much about the boy's welfare. And about his father's.

She shied away from the thought. She was too tired to deal with it any more. She couldn't remember ever being so tired. She shouldn't even be driving, she thought, rolling down the window. The breeze had no effect at all.

When she came back to herself with a start, she was shocked to find herself sitting in the car in the Kincaid Industries parking lot with no recollection of the past few miles. And, according to her watch, she had to have been here for several minutes. Numbly she dragged herself out of the car, barely managing to remember the briefcase.

She leaned against the wall in the elevator all the way up to the level of Josh's office, wondering oddly at how the walls seemed to be swaying. She felt the impact of the wall against her shoulder and realized it was she who was swaying. And worse, she couldn't seem to stop; she was grateful that it was Saturday and there were few people around. She shook her head, wondering why it seemed so fuzzy.

The floor indicator flashed, and she tried to straighten up, tried to control the little tremors that had begun. She had to face Josh, give him the wired briefcase, help him set it up. Then she was going home, she promised herself again. Home. The door slid open.

He was there. Right there, in the doorway of the elevator, as if he'd been waiting for her. His expression was unreadable, like the first time she'd seen him. Or maybe she was just too tired to read it.

No, he was angry. They had argued, hadn't they? The last time they'd talked? About...what? God, why couldn't she think? Something about him being tired of hearing ...what? Her? She studied him, her head cocked at an angle, wondering if that sweet, precious night had just been a fevered dream. It seemed entirely possible to her foggy brain.

Josh's expression changed, his brow furrowed and something warm and alive came into the icy blue eyes.

"God, Hunter, what's wrong?"

He was there then, leading her out of the elevator and into his office. He cleared a chair, gently prodded her into it. Then he knelt beside it, looking up at her.

"Hunter," he said urgently, "what is it?"

There was something she was supposed to tell him, she thought numbly. What was it? And why couldn't she stop shaking?

"I—" She stopped, shook her head sharply, wondering what this fog was that had taken over her. Josh was staring at her. Jason, she thought suddenly, he thought it was about Jason. "It's not Jason."

There. That was better. She'd said it.

"Then what?"

She stared at him. There was more? Of course there was, she chided herself. Get it said.

"Lab reports," she said. "Nothing. Just type B blood."

There. That was it. She could rest now. No, she couldn't. The case. She had to show him the briefcase. She went to reach for it, then realized she'd never let it go.

Josh, kneeling beside the chair, looked up into her face and realized he'd never seen anyone look so tired. Her eyes were huge, darkly circled, and the clear, vivid green looked muddy and haggard. Against the unnatural ashen tinge of her skin, they looked bruised and beaten. She was exhausted, he realized, down to her last spark of resistance. He'd never seen her like this, beaten, defeated. It clawed at him. And scared him.

"The case," she mumbled in that odd, slurred tone. "You close it...like this...to activate...push that lever."

She was running on nerves alone, all her vast reserves of strength depleted, he thought, but she wouldn't quit. His stomach knotted.

"Come on," he said, standing up suddenly. "You're getting out of here."

"Sorry. You said here."

He looked blank for a moment, then realized she thought he meant he didn't want her here. "You're exhausted, Hunter," he said softly. "You need rest."

"But the money...the case."

"Forget it. We'll do it in the morning. We'll have plenty of time. You need sleep."

"Home," she said suddenly. "I want to go home."

Josh's chest tightened, and his eyes stung at the simple longing in her voice. She had run herself ragged, had pushed herself to the verge of collapse, for Jason, and for him. He slipped an arm around her and gently pulled her to her feet.

"Then you'll go home, little one," he whispered.

An hour later he was driving slowly, looking for the number she'd managed to give him before she had sagged against him in the elevator. He'd carried her to the car and placed her with gentle care in the front seat. He'd thought of the back, but gruffly admitted to himself that he wanted her with him. He'd almost regretted the decision when she had wound up with her cheek snuggled on his thigh, knowing he was helpless to stop his body's reaction, but something about the way she had trusted him made the physical torture worth it.

It was a small, cozy house, tucked back against a hillside in an unincorporated canyon area of north Orange County. It sat amid a riot of plants and flowers that spoke of a loving hand. She had told him once she had bought it after her son's death because she had loved the site and because it had needed enough work to keep her busy.

He'd had the presence of mind to get her keys before she'd toppled into his arms, and he unlocked the door and propped it open to carry her inside. He found the bedroom and laid her gently on the big four-poster bed. He decided he'd had enough hell already and only slipped her shoes off before pulling the covers over her, leaving her in the slacks and thick sweater she wore. Then he looked around.

He was amazed at how comfortable he felt. The little house was welcoming in a way he'd forgotten a home could be. It was full of rich, deep colors and the warmth of natural wood, but it was the wealth of small, personal touches that made it unique. A handmade afghan on the comfortable sofa, an exquisite needlepoint picture of an eagle in flight on the wall above it and a thick, jewel-toned Navajo rug on the floor. And a basket containing a half-knitted sweater on the floor beside a big, overstuffed chair spoke of a totally unexpected side of Hunter Garrett.

He came to a halt when, after having wandered into the second bedroom—which served as a den of sorts—he found a photo of Hunter at her graduation from the sheriff's academy. The sight of her in full dress uniform, gun and baton in polished evidence, a stiff, formal expression on her lovely face beneath the carefully set hat, had him nonplussed for a moment.

Then his eyes strayed to a small photo in a silver frame, and the only emotion he felt was an infinite sadness. It was a child, barely a toddler, and he hadn't needed a label to tell him it was Timmy Garrett; Hunter's eyes were looking back at him from the color print. It must have been taken just before the boy's tragic death, and he had to turn away from it, so strong was the ache that rose in him.

He sat in that overstuffed chair for a long time, trying not to think of anything, most especially that room down the hall, and not succeeding very well. He gave his mind permission to release, to drift into sleep, but it wouldn't slow down and he remained awake.

He didn't know how much time had passed, only that it was quiet and dark now, when a sound drew his eyes to the doorway that led to her bedroom, the room that had made him wish there had been a lockable seat belt on the chair he was in.

She stood there, looking almost ethereal in the pale wash of moonlight that came through the windows whose drapes still hung open. His throat tightened, as did his body when he saw she had slipped off the slacks and wore only the soft, thick sweater that barely covered the gentle curve of her buttocks.

"Josh?"

Her voice was soft and warm and full of invitation, and he groaned inwardly. He could fight himself, but he couldn't fight her, as well, not when she stood there looking so lovely and soft and wanting. Then she held her arms out to him and he went to her as if on a string.

He kissed her with every bit of longing and need that he'd been suppressing, hungrily, fiercely, and she responded in kind. He crushed her to him, sliding his hands down her back. When his caressing fingers found her bottom bared beneath the softness of the sweater, he groaned aloud.

"Hunter, no. You said we... You were right, we can't. But God, I want you!"

"I need you," she whispered.

As if she wasn't sure she'd convinced him, her fingers began plucking at the buttons of his shirt, tugging at the buckle of his belt, the zipper of his slacks. Her eagerness stunned him, then fired him, and he moved to help her.

When he had pulled free of his clothes, he reached for her, but she backed away, into the bedroom. He followed, unable to do anything else. She let her eyes trail over him, over the broad, muscled chest, the flat, ridged stomach, down the arrow of dark hair from his navel to the widening thatch between his long, leanly muscled legs, focusing on the full, rigid flesh that had filled her so completely on the night she knew now was no dream. "Yes," she said softly.

"Yes what?" he asked thickly, aware that every muscle in his body was rippling under her gaze as surely as they did under her touch.

"You're as beautiful as I remember," she said simply.

He grabbed her then, tugging the sweater over her head, feeling a sharp, hot stab of pleasure at finding her breasts naked as well beneath it. He lifted his hands to cup them, his eyes watching hotly as they rounded into his palms and his blood leaping as she twisted sinuously against him, a low sound rising from her throat.

With amazing speed the fire flared again, the rekindled blaze even hotter for the time they'd spent trying to tamp it down. She moved to trail her mouth over him, and Josh felt a shudder ripple through every muscle in his body. He groaned again, his hands clutching at her sides as she pressed white-hot kisses over his chest and her hands slipped teasingly over the rest of him.

They went down to the bed together, but Hunter twisted so that she could press him back against the tossed pillows and flick her tongue over his chest and belly. He reached to cup her breasts once more, and she moaned when his fingers found and tugged at her taut nipples. Then her mouth found his own nipples, teasing and caressing them with her tongue until he was gasping, twisting beneath her frantically.

"Lord, Hunter, I can't wait, please," he panted.

"Help me," she whispered.

His hands went to her hips, and he lifted her over him. She straddled him eagerly, and when he would have eased her down on his aching shaft, she instead moved quickly, taking him in with fierce suddenness that made him cry out with the pleasure of it. God, she was so tight, so hot, and she was taking all of him, so deep....

Hunter rocked on him, a moan rising from the depths of her as she marveled at the feel of him. She was torn between the pleasure of having him so full and hot and hard inside her, and wanting the thrilling shock of his body's invasion of hers all over again. At last that want grew to be undeniable, and she lifted herself up until she had nearly lost him, then took him fiercely inside her again.

A sharp little cry broke from her, his name in ringing tones of pleasure that set his blood boiling along every vein. She rose up again, her hands clutching at his shoulders for balance, her breasts bobbing with the movement. Josh thought he would explode if she did that again, and when she did, the resultant shock wave ripped through him like wildfire and a guttural sound burst from him as her body slapped against his. He knew what she wanted now, and suddenly he wanted it, too, wanted to drive away the ghosts with the force of their passion. When she lifted herself again, his hands went to her hips and he added his own strength to hers as she came down on him again.

"Oh, Josh!"

He'd never thought to hear his name like that, cried out as if it were the only solid thing in a wildly spinning world. With hands suddenly frenzied, he urged her upright, the very movement driving him fully, deeply inside her. He didn't wait for her to move this time, but lifted her himself. Then he brought her down hard, arching up at the same time, bringing them together with a driving power that nearly sent him spiraling over the edge with that one stroke.

He bit his lip and held on desperately; every cry of pleasure that burst from her made it worth the strain that was beginning to make the blood hammer in his ears. Again and again he lifted and dropped her on his rigid, throbbing flesh. And again and again he felt her hands move to cover his where they gripped her hips, urging him on. Their bodies slammed together, each hammering thrust punctuated by a moaning gasp of delight from her, a harsh, near growl of pleasure from him.

Hunter knew she was dying. No one could possibly take this much sensation, this much feeling, this much pleasure and survive. He was killing her, stabbing her to her very soul, and she was glorying in it. Her body was singing, flying. When she felt the rising heat of him boiling up, heard the cry of her name that ripped sweet and hot from his throat, she gave up her grip on the world and went sailing out into blinding white space.

The only thing Josh knew was the slender body in his hands; the rest of his world had splintered away, shattered into a million fragments of crystal that danced crazily in the erupting flare of light. He thought it would go on forever, this throbbing explosion, that he would pour into her until she held all of him safe inside her, until there was no difference between them anymore. It didn't matter; it was good and right, and he was home at last.

For a long time he just lay there quietly, savoring the slight weight of her on him, stroking her hair gently. She lay with her cheek pressed against his chest, her gradually slowing breathing warm on his skin. He knew the moment when she slipped into sleep, and smiled as he held her close. The last of his barriers had been charred to ashes, as had his ability to kid himself about what he felt.

He loved her. Just thinking the words made his throat grow tight and his eyes sting. He loved her. He wanted to wake her to tell her, but she needed the rest so desperately, he didn't. And after a while he followed her into blessed oblivion.

Chapter 16

Hunter awoke to the dimness of the predawn sky and the warmth of Josh beside her. His presence felt utterly right, and she sighed inwardly. Her resistance had faded to nothing; she wanted and needed this man sleeping beside her, so much that nothing else mattered, not her past tragedy, not her work, not the rules she had always lived by.

His arm was around her, his leg thrown over hers, and she had to move carefully to disentangle herself without waking him. He needed sleep; today was going to be hell on him no matter what happened.

She stood for a moment, looking down at him, at the tousle of dark hair and the thick, lowered lashes. He looked so very vulnerable yet infinitely sexy. She tried to summon up her certainty that being involved with him was wrong, but it had been charred to cinders in the sweet, dark hours of this night. He was worth throwing away the rules for, and nothing that happened now could change that.

With another sigh she pulled on a robe and walked to the living room, suppressing a shiver of honeyed sensation as she passed the clothes Josh had discarded so hastily last night. Resolutely she pushed away the memories that brushed at her with sweet, soft butterfly wings; she had to concentrate on Jason, or those precious memories would turn sour with guilt.

She wasn't sure what good it was going to do to go over it all again, but she had some vague hope that having at last had some rest might make a difference. Armed with that hope and the memory of her rather vague thought about counting up all the information, she sat down in the middle of the floor with the thick, dog-eared file in one hand and three marking pens in the other.

She sorted the stack of papers once more into categories, field interview cards from the door-to-door checks, names, car registrations and her own extensive notes. She uncapped the yellow marking pen and began to go through every piece of the mass of information before her, marking anything that hadn't already been eliminated in her investigation. Then came the blue pen to mark anything that appeared more than once. The green one, for three or more mentions of the same car, location or piece of information, was used rarely.

With a smile she separated the items having to do with Rob Barrington; no need to keep those anymore, thanks to Josh.

"You're quite a guy, Josh Kincaid," she murmured quietly, feeling again that unfamiliar tug of proprietary pride.

Her smile widened as she set aside the computer printout on Rob's motorcycle, remembering the day he had roared past them. She wondered if he'd slow down on the thing now. He'd have to do a lot of growing up in a hurry, she thought, but with Josh's help, he could do it. She went back to the rest of the piles of papers, marking, noting.

"Good morning."

She froze, her hands clenching involuntarily around the notepad that held the just-finished list of all the items marked with the brightly colored pens. Slowly she turned her head to look at him.

"Hi," she said softly, her eyes drinking in the sight of him in the doorway, his lean body at a casually sexy angle as he leaned one shoulder on the doorjamb. He'd grabbed a towel and knotted it around his slim waist; if it was supposed to make her forget about what was beneath it, it was failing miserably.

A faint line appeared between his dark brows as his eyes flicked over the small mountain of papers that surrounded her.

"Haven't you been over that enough?"

She shrugged, tearing her eyes away from the alluring expanse of naked chest and long, leanly muscled legs.

"I keep hoping I'll find it. My gut knows it's there, but my brain can't seem to find it."

"It?"

"The one piece that will make it all fall together."

The faint line deepened to a furrow as he crossed the room and knelt before her.

"Hunter?"

She looked up.

"Going over all this again, it isn't because... You're not feeling guilty, are you?"

She flushed, lowering her eyes. "No," she said huskily. "Not anymore. I can't. It was...too beautiful."

She heard his sharp exhalation, heard him utter something that sounded like "Thank God." With an unsteady hand, she tore off the list she'd made.

"Hunter, I—"

"Not now, Josh. I meant it when I said I don't feel guilty, but we've got to think of Jason now. Only Jason."

After a moment he nodded. "Later, then," he said, and there was a world of promise in his voice. It sent a shiver up her spine and set to glowing an ember of warmth deep inside her.

Hastily she began to gather up the separate stacks of papers. "We've got to get going. I need to get to the van at the park, and we need to set up the briefcase. The money's at your office?"

He nodded. "It's in the safe. And your car's there, too."

She blushed anew. "I...Thank you for bringing me home. I was...tired."

"That," he said wryly, "is the understatement of all time." Then his tone softened. "You push yourself so hard, Hunter. Too hard."

She looked startled. "It's for Jason."

"I know."

He wanted to go on, to tell her what he had admitted to himself last night. But he knew she was right; they could think only of Jason now. There would be time enough, he thought, to tell her that she had come to mean as much to him as the precious son he'd come so close to losing. He refused to acknowledge that he could still lose that son today if anything went wrong. Nothing would go wrong; Hunter would see to that.

They showered and dressed quickly, Josh stifling another qualm as he watched Hunter strap the small but lethal two-inch .38 to her slender ankle, then tug her jeans down to cover it. It reminded him harshly of the reality this day would bring, and drove from his mind the last lingering wish that they could have had all the time in the world this morning, that he could have joined her in that steaming shower, that he could have taken her straight back to the big four-poster bed and eased this ache for her that seemed never ending.

"We'll be using a parabolic sound mike from the van," she explained as he drove, although they'd been through it all before. "It's safer than you wearing a wire, and since the drop site is flat and open, there should be no problem with any interference. We should pick up anything you say."

He nodded, a slight tightening of his hands on the wheel the only sign of a growing tension.

"We'll be ready to roll just in case he tries to pull anything, like making you go somewhere else for the drop."

"You think he will?"

"No. He won't want to show himself, so it will probably go just as planned. He'll have Jason somewhere where you can see him, but far enough away so that he'll have time to check the money before you can get to him."

"Do you think he'll really have a gun on Jason?"

His voice was remarkably steady, she thought. "We have to assume he meant what he said. That's why," she said reassuringly, "we don't move on him until we know Jason's safe."

"Garrett's law?"

She cringed.

"Hunter, I didn't mean—"

"No." She took a deep breath. "You were right, you know. All that...mystique stuff. I didn't want to admit it at first, but it's true. I'd started to believe it myself. Even be proud of it." She shook her head, the memory of that ugly self-realization clear in her eyes. "I let it get in the way of my job, and as a result I was unfair to you. I'm sorry."

Josh stared at her. Never in her life had Cynthia apologized; she would have sooner given up her credit cards. And never, ever would she have admitted the kind of error in her ways that Hunter had just so honestly done, let alone try to change it. And he realized now that she had done just that, had taken pains to explain it all to him, the off-the-wall questions, the incomprehensible mind leaps, all the things that had built her reputation.

He jerked his gaze back to the road. "You're...amazing, Hunter Garrett. And you deserve that reputation."

She made an angry little sound. "If I deserved it, Jason would be safe at home already."

"He will be," Josh said tightly; he couldn't let himself think otherwise. It was beginning to close in on him, and the tension expanded inside him. The car began to pick up speed.

"Take it easy," Hunter cautioned as the tires squealed around a turn. "We can't help Jason if we don't get there."

He backed off the accelerator. "Sorry," he said wryly. "I don't usually drive like that."

"I know." She thought of the papers on Rob she'd shuffled aside this morning. "It's usually a teenage disease. Like Rob and that bike of his."

Josh managed a fleeting grin. "He drives a company car like that, he's fired."

"Maybe he'll be safer on four wheels," she said lightly. "Although I'm afraid it's endemic to teenage boys. They all seem to do it."

"Peeling rubber as a sign of manhood," Josh agreed with a fairly steady chuckle as they pulled into the parking lot.

He went to his own reserved parking spot this time. His heart was beginning to hammer in his chest, and he barely kept himself from glancing at his watch for the fifth time in as many minutes. In three hours he would have Jason back. He would. He had to believe that.

He glanced at Hunter as he reached to turn off the ignition, and sucked in a breath at her expression. She was utterly still, and her face was shockingly pale.

"Hunter?"

"Hurry," she said suddenly, grabbing with an almost desperate movement at the crammed-full folder that lay on the floorboards at her feet.

"What is it?"

"I'm not sure yet. But hurry."

She was strung so tightly he was sure that if it had been any less than fifteen floors, she would have run up the stairs. She ran ahead of him and waited impatiently for him to unlock the office doors. She ignored the table strewn with documents and blueprints and dropped to the floor, clawing through the pile of papers, searching.

"God, Hunter—"

"Wait," she snapped, "I don't know yet." She dragged out one paper, then another, then the list she'd made. "Get the money into the case. We'll set the tracking device later."

It was an order, sharp, terse and tossed over her shoulder at him. He stared for a moment, then went to do as she said. He kept glancing at her, wary of her sudden intensity. Opening the safe behind his back, he stacked the money neatly in the briefcase. He supposed it was a fortune to some; to him it was a small price to pay to get Jason back.

He was just snapping the case closed when Hunter scrambled to her feet and ran to the phone. She dialed faster than he could see the numbers.

"This is Garrett. I need a DMV check for vehicles registered to someone."

The name she gave sounded vaguely familiar, but Josh couldn't remember why. Before he could ask, whoever she was talking to came back on the line and Hunter was rapidly scribbling notes.

"What—" he began as she hung up.

"Josh, please. I don't know yet. It's just something...."

He subsided as she dug into the file once more, coming up with a business card with the county seal on it. She flipped it over and quickly dialed the handwritten number on the back.

"Judge Clark, please. Investigator Garrett, sheriff's office, calling."

Judge? Josh leaned forward.

"Yes, I know it's Sunday morning. It's an emergency."

Josh drew in a breath to speak, then stopped as she began to dig frantically through the stack of papers that were covered in her own handwriting. She was obviously searching for something in particular, and interrupting her wasn't going to help. He reined in his burgeoning curiosity and kept silent.

"Yes, sir," she said suddenly into the phone. "I'm sorry to bother you—" A pause, then she continued, "Yes, it is the Kincaid case. I may have something, but I'll need an order from you for a release on some medical records." Another pause. "No, sir, just a blood type. On a possible suspect. He was treated—" she looked at the handwritten note she'd found "—sometime in March, after a fistfight."

She gave the same name she'd given before. Josh stared at her, suddenly as tense as she was.

"Yes, we have something to match it against." A trace of urgency crept into her respectful tone. "I'm afraid time is of the essence, sir. The ransom drop is set for—" she glanced at her watch "—less than three hours from now."

She caught her lip between her teeth; it made Josh realize his jaw was clenched so tightly it hurt.

"Yes, sir, I believe a telephonic subpoena is the only way. Coast

Hospital. Yes, I have the number to medical records." She gave the phone number, then waited another moment. "Yes. I understand. I'll be at this number for half an hour." Josh heard her rattle off his office number. "Thank you very much, sir. I'm sorry for having to disturb you."

She stared at the phone for a moment after she hung up.

"What is it?"

Josh's voice was low and harsh, and she reluctantly raised her gaze to his face. "Josh, please. I can't tell you anything yet—"

She broke off as his eyes went suddenly chilly. "Can't? Or won't?"

She went pale, but held his gaze steadily. "Don't you see?" she whispered. "What if I'm wrong? I did that once before, told you too soon, and I was wrong. I built your hopes up and then destroyed them. I can't do that to you again. I couldn't stand it."

The ice faded from the blue eyes. "Why?" he asked softly.

"Wh-what?"

He'd caught her off guard, and for a split second the truth flared in her eyes. Josh felt his heart leap, and only the thought of Jason kept him from dragging her into his arms then and there.

"It wasn't your fault before," he said finally, a little roughly. "You weren't wrong."

"But it was too late. And I might be on the wrong track now—"

"I'll take that chance."

"Josh—"

I love you, Hunter, he thought. "I trust you, Hunter," he said. "And that includes your instinct, your hunches, or whatever you want to call them. I don't know how, but Hunter's Way works."

She took in a shaky breath, staring at him as if she'd heard the words he hadn't spoken.

"Who's Dirk?" he asked gently, repeating the name she'd given.

She couldn't deny him. She'd broken every other rule of professional ethics when it came to Josh Kincaid—why not this one?

"He's the pitcher on the baseball team."

Josh's brows shot upward. "That kid?"

"I know, it sounds crazy." She gestured at the chaotic tumble of papers now strewn across his office floor. "But his is the only name that keeps popping up. The only one in green."

He looked blank. "Green?"

Quickly she explained the system. "He's here," she said, pointing to one pile, "in Rob's statement. He was the one who was supposed to come for him the night we picked him up instead. He's here—'' she pointed to a second stack ''—in my notes from the team. He kept calling Rob the 'poor little rich kid,' and Jason 'the poor littler, rich kid.'''

Josh winced but said nothing. She leaned over and picked up a third group of papers.

''And he's in here, in Ed Sterling's interviews, a couple of times. He had a fight with Rob. Started it, Ed said. And he also said Dirk drank beer a lot. The kind the team drank, when they thought he wasn't looking. The kind in the can we found in the pool house.''

Josh felt like his head was reeling, she was moving so quickly. ''How did you...?'' he began a little weakly.

''When you said that about peeling rubber. Ed said that, too, about Dirk. That he was always peeling out in that car of his. I saw it at the ball field one day, but—'' she made a disgusted sound ''—I didn't put it together until you said that.''

''Put...what together?'' He was feeling a little breathless.

''The clerk at the convenience store said she saw a beat-up, old, yellow car parked near the pay phone at about the right time. Dirk's car is a beat-up, yellow, '67 Mustang.''

Josh took in an audible breath. ''Hunter—''

They both jumped as the phone rang. It was the line she'd given to Judge Clark, and she snatched the receiver hurriedly.

''Garrett!'' Josh held the breath he'd taken while she listened, then gave several short, sharp answers to what was obviously a string of questions. ''Yes. My ID number is 1440. Lt. Lindsay. Yes, you'll have a written copy of the subpoena Monday morning.'' Josh saw her slender fingers tighten on the receiver as she listened again. Then she said, ''Thank you. Thank you very much.''

She hung up with exaggerated care. Josh didn't speak. He just waited, and after a moment her gaze lifted to his.

''Dirk's blood type is B.''

The breath he'd been holding came out on a hiss. ''The same.''

She nodded. ''The beer can and the chili. And only about ten percent of the population has that blood type.''

Josh was standing rigidly straight now, his hands clenched into fists.

''It fits,'' he said harshly. ''He went to pick up Rob...''

''Yes. And when Rob wasn't there, because we'd picked him up, he went looking around.''

''And found Jason.''

''Yes. If Jason told him he was just hiding, it wouldn't have been much of a jump for him to think of cashing in. Maybe he even thought he could get Rob blamed for it." She glanced at the briefcase. "A million dollars might not be that much compared to the worth of Kincaid Industries, but it would be the world to a sixteen-year-old."

"And that's why it was so easy, on the phone..."

She nodded. "You'd intimidate any sixteen-year-old I know, even on the phone. And maybe the reason for the wait until Saturday was something simple. Like school."

Josh's brow furrowed. "But why would he care about that? He kidnapped Jason, for God's sake."

"The school has a policy of calling home when kids don't show up. Maybe he was afraid of calling any attention to himself."

She picked up the page where she had written the registration information on Dirk's car, looked at it again, then began to gather up the rest of the papers.

"You're going to his house."

It wasn't really a question, but she nodded anyway.

"I'm going with you."

"No."

"If Jason's there—"

"There's no guarantee he has him there. He may be hiding him somewhere else. And you have to be at the park for the drop."

"But we know Dirk has him—"

"We *know* nothing. It's a string of circumstantial evidence hung together by a hunch."

"A Garrett hunch," Josh said quietly. "Isn't that enough?"

"No."

"What happened to your faith in your success ratio?"

She turned to face him then. "This isn't about numbers. This is about Jason." And you, she added silently, not knowing that the words shone in her eyes. "And I'm not going to trust his life to a hunch."

"No." Josh's voice was low, vibrant with the realization of what she was admitting, "but I am."

"Josh," she began, shaken by his faith.

"There's time. It's still more than two hours before the deadline. Let's go."

Hunter pulled to a stop out of sight of the house, still wondering what had possessed her to allow this. She should never have let him come. Not Josh. Not only was it a violation of more department policies than she could count, but also she knew if she was wrong again, if she'd once more built up his hopes only to see them come crashing down around him again, she'd never forgive herself.

She radioed Sam, who was already at the small park with the team who would be standing by. He sounded surprised when she filled him in, but never questioned her choice to delay her arrival at the drop site.

"I'll break a two-man, marked unit from the perimeter here to assist." Sam's voice crackled out of the small speaker. "We'll stand by here. Just make sure Kincaid gets here in time if this doesn't pan out."

"Ten-four, will advise as soon as I have anything," she acknowledged, then shut off the radio.

"He might already be on his way," she warned Josh, "or even already there, waiting."

"I know," Josh said, unperturbed.

"It might not even be Dirk."

"But you think it is."

She sighed. "Yes."

"Okay."

She stared at him. When had things got so turned around? Now he was the one who believed in that damn Garrett mystique while she was the one who was in a quagmire of doubt.

"We getting out, or what?"

Her forehead creased. "I am. You—"

"—will be right behind you."

"Josh—"

"We're just looking around, right? Save that 'no' for when you really need it."

Hunter sighed. "You," she said succinctly, "make me crazy."

"I sincerely hope so."

There was no sign of a double entendre in his voice or face, but Hunter felt herself color anyway.

"Only until the other unit gets here," she capitulated stiffly. "Then you let us handle it." If there's anything to handle, she thought rather grimly.

"Of course."

She backed up the unmarked car until it was blocking the alley entrance, then got out. She walked to the back and took a small portable radio out of the trunk and stuffed it in the back pocket of her jeans. She spared a glance for the innocent-looking briefcase. Josh caught her look.

"Be a hell of a surprise if somebody stole the car, wouldn't it?"

She couldn't stop the grin that flashed across her face. He was incredible, she thought, this man she loved. Her breath caught in her throat as the words flitted through her mind, fully formed and glowing, as if they'd been there all the time if she'd only dared to look. She'd known she wanted him, needed him, but love? Oh, Lord, she thought, what a time for *that* revelation.

She slammed the trunk closed with a bit more vehemence than necessary. They walked around the corner to just within sight of Dirk's house. It was an older one, just on the edge of the city limits of Aliso Beach. The difference between here and the opulent expanse of Josh's neighborhood was blatantly obvious.

Her eyes went over the exterior quickly but thoroughly. There were no lights on, no sign of life. The curtains at all the windows were open, a small hint that if Jason was here, he wasn't in the house. They watched for several minutes; nothing changed.

"Let's check the alley," she said softly, and without a word Josh followed her when she turned and headed back the way they had come.

The alley was deserted, a narrow strip of asphalt lined by a hodgepodge of fences of various heights and materials. Just as she spotted a section of the same worn, wooden fence that had been in front of Dirk's house, Josh touched her shoulder. She followed the direction of his gaze. Her eyes narrowed when she saw, barely visible on the far side of the closed garage to Dirk's house, a sparkle of chrome front bumper and a sliver of a yellow fender.

"Oh, boy," she breathed.

"He hasn't left yet," Josh said tightly. "That means Jason might be here."

"Maybe," she said, trying to rein in her own instinctive reaction. "He might be using another car."

Josh didn't answer. Hunter tried again. "Or Dirk might still be here because he isn't involved at all."

"You don't believe that."

It wasn't a question, and Hunter surrendered. She pulled out the radio. She turned away from the house, and her voice was low and guarded as she spoke into it. The small action kicked Josh's heart into overdrive; she was worried about being overheard. When she raised the unit Sam had sent, her instructions were clear and precise.

"Split up," she ordered, "one of you take the front of the house. The other take the north end of the alley—try and find a spot with a line of sight on the back of the house. We have the south end of the alley and the garage area."

She gave a swift description of Dirk and, with a wry look at Josh, a description of him, too.

"He's the victim's father," she said into the small radio, "so don't make any mistakes."

Josh's heart was pounding by the time the radio sparked to life again with the report that the two officers were in position.

"Maintain the perimeter," she told them. "I'm going in for a closer look."

She pushed the radio back into her pocket and began to inch forward. She sensed Josh moving behind her and twisted her head to look at him.

"Stay here." She gestured toward an overgrowth of brush that jutted out into the alley. "Use that for cover. Watch the house—I won't be able to see it."

"Hunter—"

"I'm just going to look. I'll be right back."

She was gone before he could answer, moving in a low crouch that kept her below the top of the fence. It should have looked awkward, but she gave even the unnatural motion a kind of grace. When she got even with the garage, she stopped, crouching below the building's single window; Josh could almost feel her holding her breath. When she moved again, it was with such swiftness that he sucked in and held a breath of his own.

With a quick, darting movement she raised her head to peer through the grimy window. She came back down, moving in nimble silence past the garage. Her head came up above the top of the fence for a split second as she risked a glance into the backyard. Then she was crouched and moving again, quickly, agilely. He saw her glance into the parked yellow car, then saw the slightest of hitches in her smooth movements as she looked past it.

She whirled, low and graceful, moving in a controlled rush back to the front of the Mustang. Josh stiffened when he saw her slide one slender hand through the grille just above the chrome horse of the car's logo, and winced when he heard the tiny metallic snap of the hood latch being released. What the hell? he thought.

He knew in the next second when he saw her reach under the hood she had raised a bare six inches; he saw her grab something and yank. She eased the hood back down and leaned on it until the latch caught once more. Then she was moving again, in that impossible bent run, back to him.

"What was it?" he asked harshly when she dropped down beside him once more. She hesitated, looking at him. "You saw something. What?"

Logic, training and policy all told her she should keep her mouth shut. Love told her she couldn't. Shutting him out at this point was impossible.

"A toolshed," she said tightly. "Just beyond the car. It's old, run-down...and it has a brand-new, shiny padlock on the outside."

Josh went rigid. "Jason...?"

"Maybe. I don't know. I just know that lock stands out like a strobe in the dark."

"What happens now?" His voice was tight, controlled.

"We wait." She glanced at her watch. "But in half an hour, you're out of here."

He made a protesting movement.

"No choice, Josh. You take the car and get to the park. You have to be there." She grimaced wryly. "You should be there now, but somehow I don't think I can convince you of that. Leaving then only gives you a half-an-hour margin."

His silence and the set line of his jaw was her answer. Hunter spoke briefly into the radio, advising the others of what she'd done and wanted them to do. Then she settled in to wait.

The minutes ticked off. It wasn't excessively warm out, but Josh found himself sweating. Every muscle in his body was tightened until he ached under the pressure. When she glanced at her watch once more and then raised her eyes to his, he nearly shouted a protest.

"Josh, you have to—"

The radio crackled noisily. "Movement at the back of the house!" the unseen officer at the north end of the alley said sharply.

"Copy," Hunter answered quickly. "Move in slow, low and out of sight. When you lose cover, stop."

She turned down the volume on the radio, just in case. She could feel Josh's tension, felt it nearly snap when she reached down to free her two-inch handgun from the ankle holster. She tucked the gun into the waistband of her jeans, then turned her gaze steadily on Josh.

"This is the 'no' you've been waiting for, Josh. Let us do our job."

"I—"

"You shouldn't even be here. We're trained for this. I can't concentrate on Jason if I have to worry about you, too." She saw the anguish in his face, the torture in his eyes. "I know it will be the hardest thing you've ever done, to just...wait. But trust me, it has to be this way."

His expression changed as she asked for his trust. The pain faded, and something else took its place, something so warm and alive it took her breath away.

A noise from down the alley spun her around. It was the high-pitched creak of neglected hinges. A moment later there was a metallic sound, then the static-distorted spit of the radio.

"He's at the car. Put something in the trunk. Can't see what."

Josh snapped upright. Hunter grabbed his wrist. With the greatest effort he'd ever made in his life, he sank back. And with that movement he put his future in Hunter's hands.

She darted across the alley, into the tiny hidden space below the garage window. Josh crouched behind the concealing brush, barely daring to breathe. He saw a movement up the alley out of the corner of his eye. He heard the slam of a car door, and nearly screamed with the frustration of not being able to see any more.

The ineffective grinding of the starter told him Hunter had effectively disabled the car. Ignition wires, he guessed, remembering the yanking motion of her arm. Then a shouted curse froze him and he stared, wide-eyed, as the tall, gangly blond teenager stalked angrily around to the front of the car and opened the hood.

Incredibly Hunter came out from behind the garage and walked toward Dirk as casually as if she were just out for a Sunday stroll.

"Car trouble?"

Her soft inquiry floated back to Josh in the same moment that Dirk jerked upright, rapping his head sharply on the underside of the open hood. In that split second Hunter had moved, bringing the hood down firmly but not cripplingly atop the startled teenager's hands.

"Son of a—"

"It's over, Dirk. All over."

"I don't know what the hell you're talking about!"

It was all Josh could do not to burst from his hiding place. But he saw the uniformed officer approaching and wisely stayed put. Hunter would handle it, he thought, fighting down his fierce need for action. In some distant corner of his mind, he was acknowledging how much he truly did trust her. He trusted her with Jason's life. With his life.

"You can't do this!" Dirk exclaimed as the uniformed officer came up behind him. Hunter released the pressure on the hood. The moment the young blond yanked his hands free, the officer pulled them back into his waiting handcuffs.

"Smooth as silk, Garrett," he said with a grin as the cuffs clicked home. "You haven't lost your touch."

Without a word Hunter whirled and ran around the car. Josh told himself he could move now, but he couldn't seem to get his legs to listen. He saw her reach into the car and grab the keys, then disappear out of sight.

After one agonizingly frozen moment, she reappeared, a small shape clad in grubby jeans and shirt huddled in her arms. Her head was lowered, and he could hear the soft, reassuring croon of her voice even though he couldn't make out the words.

Josh still couldn't make himself move. His eyes were swimming, and he couldn't swallow past the lump in his throat. As she walked across the alley, Hunter whispered something to the child in her arms, then lowered him to the ground. He looked at her, then at his father.

"Daddy?" he said doubtfully, and the tone of uneasiness in his voice was the impetus Josh needed to get his shocked muscles to respond. He covered the distance between them in one long stride and swept the boy up into his arms.

"Jason," he said brokenly, over and over as he hugged the boy close. It was a long time before he could stop.

Hunter felt her throat tighten as she watched Jason throw his arms around his father's neck and hug him back fiercely. This, she thought, was what made the job worth it all. But she knew this was more than her usual joy at a reunion she had helped to bring about; this was joy at the reuniting of the man she loved with his son.

"Daddy?" Jason Kincaid's voice was full of wonder as he leaned back in his father's arms and looked at him. "Are you crying?"

Josh blinked rapidly, meeting the pair of wide, cinnamon-colored eyes he'd feared never to see again, eyes that were looking at him with a wonder that surpassed that in his voice. Wonder, Josh realized with painful clarity, that his father was crying over him.

"Yes," he said finally, simply. "God, Jason, I've been so scared."

"Scared?" Jason's wonder grew to astonishment. "You? You're never scared."

"I was. For you. I'm so sorry. For everything. I love you, Jason."

"You do?"

Josh couldn't answer.

"I wanted to come home," Jason said almost shyly.

"I know," Josh choked out. "We found your note."

"I was going to tell Rob. That's why I waited." The boy made a face, an eloquent expression of distaste. "I didn't want to go with Dirk, but he made me."

"I know. It's all right."

"You're not mad?"

"I'm just glad you're safe. Things are going to change, Jason." He gave his son a slightly wobbly smile. "Think you can teach me about being a father?"

Jason's warm brown eyes widened as his mouth rounded into an O of surprise. "Me?"

"I've got a lot to learn. But we've got time, now. Lots of time, for just the two of us. Think you can handle that?"

Hunter felt a twinge she didn't like but couldn't deny. Josh hadn't said a word to her since she'd pulled Jason from the trunk of Dirk's car. She turned away, inwardly chastising herself as she took out the small radio to advise Sam that the wait was over, Jason was safe. Then she turned back to look at the rapt father and son, rediscovering each other, and tried to recover the joy she seemed to have lost.

What did you expect, Garrett? You break the rules, you pay the price. And boy, did you break the rules. Professionally and personally.

She was staring out into her yard, noticing idly that the garden needed work. No energy, she thought with a sigh. Figures. The lieutenant orders me to take a vacation, *then* I get tired.

Well, not exactly. She'd been tired since they'd recovered Jason. After spending the rest of that Sunday at the hardest part of her job, making the way she arrived at her conclusions look logical on paper, she'd smothered her reservations and gone to the house to see Josh. She was being too sensitive, she'd decided, unsure of his feelings.

She'd been met by an ebullient Mrs. Elliott, who threw her arms around her and hugged her. "I knew you would do it! Thank you so much for bringing Jason back to us!" The woman was going on before Hunter could get a word out. "I declare, I've never seen anything like Jason and Mr. Josh today, laughing and yelling like they were both Jason's age."

She had smiled. She remembered that, because it was the last time she had smiled. A smile that had faded as Mrs. Elliott had gone on.

"Mr. Josh is going to take some time off, so they can spend it together. Jason is so excited. They're out to dinner now, the two of them, planning what to do."

And that, Hunter told herself now, was that. Father and son were together again. Complete. Just the two of them, he'd said. And he'd meant it. Not even a word from him in days made that more than clear. Josh had needed her, but he didn't anymore. She was the fool who had fallen in love. But, God, she missed him!

At least he didn't know. She had turned the loose ends of the case over to Sam so she could do what she had to do—walk away, as she had countless times before. She would leave Josh and Jason to rebuild their lives, to forget the narrowly averted tragedy. It was part of the job, and she accepted it. If it was harder this time, then she had no one to blame but herself. Never once had he said he loved her.

She pulled herself out of the chair, resolutely smothering the little voice that was trying to cry out in protest, trying to say that even if he hadn't said it, nothing but love could have been behind his tender care of her the night she had reached the end of her endurance.

She headed for the kitchen to fix another meal she knew she wouldn't eat. At a sharp rap on the door, she turned around. Sam, she supposed, with another ton of questions. She pulled open the door.

"Hi," Jason said calmly, looking at her from his perch on his father's broad shoulders. The memory of that picture on Josh's desk tightened her throat, and she could barely speak.

"Hel—hello." Her eyes flicked hungrily to Josh, savoring the new lightness in his eyes even as she felt the tug of pain.

"We need to know if you have a suitcase," Jason said.

"What?" She looked at the boy, confused.

"A suitcase," Josh repeated, his voice oddly husky. "You know, to pack?"

"I—Why?"

"To go on a trip, silly," Jason said blithely.

"A...trip?"

"You are on vacation, right?" Josh was looking at her avidly, as if he'd missed her as much as she'd missed him. Then he went on softly, pointedly. "Jason decided if I was going to be talking about you every second, you might as well come with us."

"We're going to the mountains. And fishing. Dad's been working real hard every day so we can leave tomorrow."

"That's...where you've been?"

"What did you think?" His expression told her he knew what she'd thought; his eyes told her it had been as hellish for him as it had been for her.

"I—"

"You do like to fish, don't you?" Jason interrupted in sudden concern.

"I—Yes."

"Oh, good," the boy said, relieved. "Then Dad won't spend the whole time missing you."

Hunter's startled gaze flew back to Josh's face. "Jason figured that out all by himself, once I told him."

"Told him?"

"That I love you," Josh said softly.

Hunter smothered a tiny exclamation as her eyes widened. Josh's eyes were fastened on her, pleading with her to understand. And suddenly she did; he had wanted Jason to come to this decision on his own, to accept her of his own accord.

"Oh, Josh! I—"

"And it has nothing to do with gratitude, either, even though I owe you more than I could ever repay."

"Josh, you don't under—"

"And I don't want to hear any of that bonding under stress stuff, either," he added sternly. "I know better."

"But—"

"Did you ever stop to think that maybe I love you in spite of the circumstances, not because of them?"

Hunter made a strangled little sound.

"Are you laughin' or cryin'?" Jason asked with interest.

"Both," she choked out, "because your father won't let me tell him that I love him, too."

Josh stared at her. "You...do?"

"Of course I do! How could I not?"

"Even," he said, his eyes flicking to Jason, "as a package deal?"

"Especially as a package deal," Hunter whispered, her eyes wide and soft and brilliantly green as tears of joy pooled in them.

* * * * *